OUR
NATURAL RESOURCES:
HOW TO
INVEST IN THEM

Our
Natural Resources:
How to
Invest in Them

by

Walter Youngquist, Ph.D.
Professor of Geology, University of Oregon
and

Consulting Geologist

FREDERICK FELL, INC.   *NEW YORK*

To the people who work
and save and invest, to make
our free-enterprise system
the success which it is.

Contents

10 CONTENTS

OUR
NATURAL RESOURCES:
HOW TO
INVEST IN THEM

Introduction

Land, air, and water will never go out of style. Combine this fact with the tremendous population rise and the great demand for investment capital to develop our natural resources to meet the needs of this population, and you have the gist of this book.

The World Health Organization in July, 1964, in a report titled "The Population Explosion" states, "For every 100 persons in the world in 1950 there will be 251 in the year 2000. At present 50-60 million people are being added to the world population each year, with the result that the world's population is doubling in approximately 23 years."

We are adding a population equivalent to that of Great Britain, France, or Italy to the world *each year*.

Demand for natural resources of all kinds can only go up.

Everything we have, even ourselves, comes from the Earth. Our industries take raw materials, process them, and combine them into TV sets, automobiles, paper, gasoline, houses, and thousands of other things which make up our standard of living. Our amazing chemical industries are virtual alchemists now—they can make something out of something else—but they still cannot make something out of nothing, nor are they ever likely to do so. They must start with some raw material. And someone, perhaps you, must invest the money needed to explore for and develop that natural resource so our industries can use it.

Fortunes have come from the Earth. Natural resources are one of the chief sources of new wealth. Guggenheim made a fortune from mining. Oil made Rockefeller a multimillionaire, Charles Steen not long ago became a rich man in the uranium boom, and International Nickel Company, Ltd., is making money right now in Canada from the world's greatest nickel deposits. The story is far from over. In fact, it is just beginning.

With the population pressures we face, the Earth's resources must now be developed on a scale far beyond anything ever seen before. We are already into this fantastically rapid development. For example, *all of the fossil fuels (coal, oil, natural gas) the world produced before the year 1900, would last less than 5 years at the current rate of world consumption.* In the United States, if we consider all of our minerals, the incredible fact is that *we have in the past 30 years used up more of these resources than we did in all previous history of the United States.*

To meet these natural resource development needs, tremendous amounts of money will have to be invested—and wisely. Our funds—your money—cannot be wasted. In my work as a geologist, people ask my opinion about investments in such things as oil wells in Kansas, mines in Idaho and Nevada, oil company stocks listed on the New York Stock Exchange, and about the merits of buying lakeshore in my native Minnesota. These are intelligent people, but their backgrounds and experiences are such as to frequently give them few ideas as to what factors go into making good investments in these natural resources.

There seemed to be a need for a book which, from a

professional viewpoint, would give easily understood advice and provide basic information as to the relative importance and probable future of these various resources.

The amount of money which must go into the development of oil, oil shale, and tar sands to supply our petroleum needs is staggering. The story is the same all along the line— paper, electric power, water supply, lumber, copper, iron. Under our free enterprise system it is *you* who must put up this money. But to get the job done, investments must be made carefully. Your money must be used to best advantage. I hope this book will aid you in the wise, efficient, and profitable use of your savings to develop our natural resources.

It is worthwhile to mention, also, that to protect your savings from the seemingly ever-present threat, as well as fact, of inflation, natural resources offer what has been in the past one of the best shelters. The current very strong investor interest in natural resources is in part, at least, due to this factor.

Investing in natural resources is a fascinating activity. It can also provide many pleasant and interesting hours, for investment can mean not only money, but investing your time and work as well. Developing marginal lands, suburban lands, and waterfront acreages into recreational areas, or to summer or permanent homesites can be a fine "do it yourself" project, which will pay rich dividends in healthy exercise, can be enjoyable, and also be profitable.

As well as giving you ideas which you can expand yourself in regard to natural resource investments, this book tells the following things about our common, and a few uncommon resources:

1. How important is the resource in our economy now, and how important is it likely to be in the future, and why?

2. How is its growth rate likely to compare with that of the demand for other natural resources, and with the growth of the economy as a whole?
3. What are the various ways in which you can invest in each resource?
4. As this volume is intended primarily for persons interested in natural resource investments in the United States and Canada, the situations of these two countries relative to the particular resource (supply and demand) are given special consideration.

United States and Canadian investors are especially fortunate, for these two countries have such a remarkable abundance and variety of natural resources lying in areas which can still be explored. *North America offers a natural resource investment spectrum unequalled in any other area of comparable size in the world.* This richness of natural resources is fortunately combined with a form of government and an economic system which allow anyone to invest in these resources—a situation envied in many other parts of the world, and a combination of circumstances which is without parallel anywhere else. Travel abroad, and you will appreciate how fortunate you are to be part of this North American continent and its economic and political systems. No one should miss the opportunity of investing, and it is gratifying to note that 20 million people in the United States have already become stockholders in our companies, both natural resource firms, and others.

Just the land itself is a prime resource. I have travelled the length of the Amazon River and seen that basin, and I have lived in Iowa; there is no comparison between the productivity of the two areas—the leached red tropical clays, compared with the fertile black Iowa loam. Foreigners recognize this great asset we have in our land, and Europeans in increasing numbers are buying land in North America, as they see what bargains we still have compared with what is available to them in Europe. North America also has some of the world's greatest deposits of coal, oil shale, nickel, iron, potash, sulfur, borax, phosphate, asbestos, gypsum, molybdenum, and many other vital materials. This is a region richly endowed with natural resources, and with great opportunities, and a great need for investment money to develop these resources.

Our Nation's progress depends, in part, on each of us intelligently investing in our natural resources. Attempts to get into space notwithstanding, the Earth is going to have to provide our living for a long time to come. While many people are looking at the Moon, wise investors will be looking beneath their feet.

Note: Companies cited in this book are used simply as examples and such references are not to be construed as recommendations. From time to time, the author may have investments in certain of the companies mentioned.

Land

"The major fortunes in America have been made in land," states the president of one company which used to get most of its revenues from oil, but found that the surface of the ground was worth more than what was underneath. The company, once principally an oil producer, now earns about three-fourths of its revenue from real estate. Goodyear Tire and Rubber Company, not usually thought of as a real estate company, is involved in developing 14,000 acres of its land in Arizona into what is expected to be a city of more than 50,000 people by 1985, and many other firms are investing in land.

But individuals have been in the land investment field for years, and as land can come in any size, this sort of investment can be found in sizes to suit most any pocketbook. Also, you can buy it with very little down (as little as 10% sometimes), as compared with listed stocks (usually the regulations demand from 50 to 100% payment).

Land as an investment has another factor in its favor. A stock may eventually be utterly worthless, and money in the bank can be lost through bank failures, but it would be a very exceptional circumstance indeed if any land you purchased would decrease in value to absolutely nothing.

More likely it seems that with present and future population pressures, it would be unusual if you bought a piece of good land at any reasonable price which would be worth any less 5 years from now than what you paid for it. Certainly many marginal stocks traded now will be worth less than the current price, 5 years from now. Although land can cost something to hold in terms of taxes, the basic value at the time you invest is almost always retained, and generally land seems to increase in value at least as fast as inflation proceeds; well-selected land will rise in price many times faster than inflation. Carefully chosen acreage is surely a prime investment.

Excerpts from two copyrighted interviews published in *U. S. News and World Report* point out the fundamental position of land, and the trends of demand and price. In an interview with Ragnar D. Noess, New York investment counselor, on the topic "How to Handle Your Money Now," (*U. S. News and World Report,* Jan. 31, 1966), Mr. Noess was asked: "What do you think of real estate as an investment?" Mr. Noess replied: "I am not a real estate expert or investor. But when I look at the population gains that are coming in the United States over the next 50 years, it seems to me that real estate prices only go one way— up. I'm talking about well-located real estate. When we consider that the eastern part of the country will be one tremendous suburban area, what can happen? I think living space is going to be one of the scarce items in man's existence." An interview with George Cline Smith, construction authority, titled "What's Happened to the Building Boom?" (*U. S. News and World Report,* Nov. 27, 1965), had this question put to Mr. Smith: "Will land values continue to rise?" Mr. Smith's reply: "They always have. Increasing land values have been the history of the world.

The only thing that would stop that would be a leveling off of population, a stable population. The more people we put on this earth, the more we divide it up, the more the cost of each square inch is going to be."

The population of North America is expected to increase 64% by the year 2000, Latin America by 157%, and Africa by 151%.

Land is a classic case of a vital material in fixed supply. It has been truly said, "They make more people but they don't make more land." Thousands of acres each year are swallowed up more or less permanently into freeways, housing developments, public parks, et cetera.

To divert at least some public attention from Moongazing and back to the Earth and our crucial land situation, the United States Department of the Interior recently published a booklet entitled "The Race for Inner Space." Now the Federal Government is setting aside large tracts as "Wilderness Areas," and a bill has been passed allowing some of our rivers to be designated as "Wild Rivers." State and Federal agencies will buy land along the rivers to hold permanently. Land also is being acquired by a number of states (Minnesota, Wisconsin, and others) as "public access" sites to lakes and rivers. Some of this land is purchased outright, some is leased for long term from landowners at an annual rental.

All these trends add up to the fact that land is one of our most basic resources, demand can only increase, the supply is in fixed amount, and prices can only go up. But some land will rise slowly in value whereas other land prices will increase more rapidly.

Various kinds of land investments are described in the following pages. Certain types of land are suggested as likely to rise in value faster than average; examples are given to show how some land situations can be made to rise in value through your own spare-time efforts and imagination.

WATERFRONT AND OTHER RECREATIONAL LAND

Among the various types of land investments to be made, lakeshore, river frontage, and other sorts of recreational land offer, in my opinion, one of the best and most interesting fields of enterprise open to the small investor. More importantly, perhaps, it may also be the most satisfying.

I have invested in both farm land and in lakeshore and have worked to develop and improve both, and hour for hour the work on the lakeshore property was far more enjoyable than working on the farm (and, interestingly enough, it has been the more profitable). Perhaps the lakeshore was more fun because when I got tired of cutting trees and clearing brush, I could go down to the lake for a cool swim, or push the canoe out a few hundred feet and cast a fly over to that bass which had been rising near the edge of the lily pads for the previous half-hour.

Writing in his column of August 6, 1965, in the *Minneapolis Tribune,* Jim Kimball came back from a vacation in northern Minnesota where he had worked on some lakeshore in which he had invested, and made these simple but profound comments which show the unique value of this sort of property:

> "Joy and satisfaction is standing on a beautiful piece of land overlooking a quiet lake and saying to yourself 'This lovely bit of natural beauty is my very own.'"

You will find waterfront development a most satisfying and pleasant venture. Aside from getting hours of good healthy exercise in what should be an increasingly nice setting as you improve the property, you should have a personal satisfaction in converting a piece of raw unused land into a place where people can come to be away from the congestion of the city. Lakeshore in particular, and waterfrontage in general, is such a valuable commodity that I think it should be developed with a special conscience about how it is done. You will almost certainly make money on such a development, but making money, in my opinion, should be secondary here to doing the task in a way that is in the best interests of everyone. The beauty of the area should be preserved; the crowding of the city should be eliminated as much as possible. In fact, doing it this way will make it more valuable property because people will want a contrast with the city—not just another city lot.

Waterfront—heirloom stuff.

Even if it were possible to support people on this Earth to the extent that they could each exist on 10 square feet of ground, would life be worth living under such conditions? I doubt it. An uncle of mine from Chicago used to visit us in the Wisconsin lake country every summer for two weeks. He lived all year for those two weeks, and I think if he had come up oftener he would have lived longer.

In Europe, lakeshore is rarely sold. If a surviving family exists, lakeshore is simply passed on from generation to generation. It pays to travel around and from what you see in one area, project these trends into other areas. By seeing trends in one place, you can recognize their small but sig nificant beginnings in another region. Lakeshore becoming heirloom stuff—there is a trend. But there is lots of lakeshore in Minnesota and in a number of other states, and I know places right now where it may be purchased for as little as $2 a front foot (waterfrontage is sold by the front foot, the depth back from the water being a secondary consideration usually). I recently purchased 43 acres with 1300 feet of shoreline on an excellent fishing lake, for $2400. I had to search for such a property, but I did find it, and in the process of looking I ran across a number of other offerings of lakeshore not greatly different in price. Good lakeshore can still be bought at reasonable figures.

Nevertheless, I was interested to learn not long ago while visiting a friend who has a cabin on Burntside Lake in the famed Arrowhead Country of northern Minnesota, that his neighbor along the lake to the east had just made a will which provided that this lakeshore could not be sold for three generations to come; if there were heirs, the lakeshore had to stay in the family. On hearing this, my friend had begun to draw up a similar will. So this European treatment of lakeshore has now reached our shores. I am convinced that lakeshore, and waterfrontage in general, is fast becoming heirloom stuff.

Mr. Leonard G. "Buck" Hedman, owner of Hedman's Resort Exchange in Grand Rapids, Minnesota, in the heart of one of the best lake districts in the United States, is a long experienced and most knowledgable dealer in lakeshore, and has several times appeared in court classed as an "expert witness" in connection with lakeshore evaluations. I have been acquainted with him for a number of years, and his views on this matter, as expressed in a recent letter, are in my opinion worth quoting. He writes, "Lakeshore property is increasing in value every year . . . the value can go nowhere but up." In an attractive brochure which Mr. Hedman publishes about Minnesota lakeshore property, he makes this statement: "It is difficult to find another investment that can match the dynamic increase in values that lakeshore property is enjoying today."

I have taken considerable time to check the trend of lakeshore prices over the United States the past 10 years, personally visiting areas in Wisconsin, Minnesota, Florida, Oregon, Idaho, and California, and everywhere my observations bear out Mr. Hedman's views. Furthermore, even in areas where at the moment lakeshore looked "fully priced," it frequently took just a year or two to make those prices look like bargains in retrospect. With the greater leisure time which people have, and the ever more crowded situation in this country, lakeshore, and waterfrontage in general, offer values which increasingly cannot really be measured in mere dollars and cents. I see no reason to believe these trends will be reversed at any very early date. Lakeshore will be in strong demand indefinitely.

Typical lakeshore development sequence.

A geographer friend of mine, Dr. Harry Caldwell of the University of Idaho, made an interesting study of the history of lakeshore and near-lake property. He found that development usually takes place in 4 rather well-defined stages. Here they are:

1. Undeveloped lakeshore is bought in fairly large tracts (20 to 100 acres or more, commonly), and a house built on each tract.

2. The original tract with the house on it is reduced in size. The house with a few hundred feet of shoreline becomes one unit. Remaining shoreline is sold off in smaller tracts. If the original owner retains a 200-foot frontage, he will usually sell off the rest in somewhat smaller pieces—the initial estate owners still like to have the largest frontage, locally.

3. Areas behind the original fringe of lakeshore are subdivided, but a few strips of access are purchased from shoreline owners so that corridors to the lake are provided for the second ring of houses. Title to these corridors, and to small areas of lakeshore where boats can be moored, are held in common by all owners of this second echelon of houses.

4. A third ring of land—a fairly wide ring in depth— is subdivided, and this is advertised as "lake view property" (all land around a lake, of course, is lake view property as the lake is at least slightly lower than the adjacent ground). This property will not have access to the lake, as the original lakeshore owners do not want to sell any remaining property as access routes, and the owners of the second ring of houses will usually not wish to further share their limited access with a third group.

After Dr. Caldwell called my attention to this pattern of development, I have been able to recognize it in a number of areas (northern Idaho, northern California, southern Wisconsin, the Minneapolis-St. Paul area, central Florida, et cetera).

Lakeshore and the word "lake" I am sure will always

have a magic touch, for with a few strokes of the paddle from shore you are in a different world. Lakeshore is prime land to increase in value.

Finding waterfrontage.

Some areas of the United States are not blessed with much waterfrontage, but many areas are. Start near home, if possible, but here the matter of distance is relative. Because of increasingly good freeways, many people from Kansas City, Des Moines, Chicago, and Indianapolis go to northern Minnesota, Wisconsin and Michigan each summer, travelling 1000 miles and more round trip.

Start by getting some maps. Excellent maps are the U. S. Geological Survey topographic maps (write the U. S. Geological Survey, Washington 25, D. C., for areas east of the Mississippi; for areas west of the Mississippi, write the USGS, Building 25, Denver Federal Center, Denver 2, Colorado, and ask for "An index map of topographic mapping" for your state. These maps are free). From this index map, order the quadrangles (as they call the maps) you want. These topographic maps are inexpensive, easy to read, and they even show buildings on them so you can readily determine what degree of development there is in various areas to the date of publication of the map. Roads are shown, as well as are many of the backwoods trails. Swamp areas are designated by easily-read symbols. These maps offer you a convenient way to study large areas quickly, from the comfort of your armchair.

Fly over the area—by means of air photos.

If you want more information, hire a small airplane and fly over the country. Take a few color slides to show on the screen in your living room—a great way to study an area in detail at your leisure. You can usually rent a plane and a pilot reasonably from a local airport. Rammco Investment Corporation of California is one of several companies which make a business of searching out land for investors. They use a helicopter. But if you can't afford an airplane or a helicopter, I have another suggestion. Do as I have done—"fly" over the country by means of air photographs. This technique applies to all land, of course, not just waterfrontage. You can get air photo index sheets (a composite of individual air photos) which cover large areas. From them, if you want more detail, you can order the individual sets of stereoscopic air photographs and with a simple pocket stereoscope (any engineering supply house sells them for a few dollars, or you can sometimes buy them at a war surplus store) you can, for all practical purposes, be flying over the area and inspecting it. With low level photos, you can even see individual trees. I have spent many pleasant winter evenings looking for land this way—using a topographic map first, then getting air photo index sheets, and then buying the stereo air photos and studying them with a stereoscope. For areas you are interested in, ask both the U. S. Geological Survey and the Department of Agriculture as to what their air photo coverage is. Much of the United States has now been "flown" for air photos.

I am waiting for the day when they put out air photos in color (they do exist now but not for general use or sale).

Then it will truly be like flying over the country to travel via air photos. But even the black and white photos are very satisfactory; hills and swamps clearly show and you can also, by the way, get a good idea of the depth of the lake or stream.

Here, I will reveal a little secret. I used to work as a guide on canoe trips in northern Minnesota and Wisconsin. Air photos helped me find reefs and sandbars which I wouldn't have known about otherwise. Bars and reefs off points on the shore are easy to predict and are heavily fished. But many unsuspected reefs and bars exist out in the central portions of some lakes and these are usually not too well known and are infrequently fished. Here is where the fish come from the deeper cooler waters of the lake to feed in the evenings. These bars and reefs show up on the air photos as very distinctive light areas and you can locate them by simple triangulation from easily identified points on shore. These shallow areas are usually not visible from a boat when you are on the lake—the reflection from the water conceals them. Only when viewed from several thousand feet up do they show, and thus the air photos show them. Want to know where the sandbars are in a lake where the walleyed pike or bass will be feeding at night? Use air photos.

But to return to our theme—how to locate undeveloped waterfrontage—the U. S. Geological Survey topographic maps, air photos, and county highway maps (write state highway department) will help you greatly. When you have located an area of interest, visit it, and if it still looks good, check with local people or with real estate dealers as to who owns the property. Here, however, it is well to keep in mind that money to be made in lakeshore chiefly involves developing and subdividing acreages. Buying already subdivided lakeshore property (that is, lots) is probably only slightly better than buying city lots, ordinarily just a fair investment.

Taxes are high, relative to the size of the piece of land, once it has been platted into lots.

But sizable acreages do exist, and can still be bought. Some of them, you will discover, have not been developed for comparatively good reasons; difficult access or lack of access is one of the chief reasons. See why the tract is not yet developed. Then make up your own mind if the reasons are fatal, or if they can be remedied with a little imagination and work on your part, or are likely to be solved by merely patiently waiting for new roads or other improvements which are planned for that area.

How to judge lake and river frontage.

When looking at waterfrontage, the following checklist may be useful to you:

1. Is the lake or river deep or shallow? Will it dry up from time to time or are the water levels subject to marked seasonal changes? Note: Artificial lakes are subject to considerable changes in level, usually. An easy and fairly reliable rule of thumb as to whether or not a lake will have a reasonably stable water level is to determine if it has a natural inlet and outlet. Ordinarily lakes with a natural inlet and a natural outlet (not a dam) fluctuate very little in level.

2. What is the nature of the shoreline? Sand is best for swimming and probably the best all around. Mud is obviously less desirable. Rocky shores with abrupt drop-offs are picturesque but not popular with families which have small children, obviously.

3. Is the land high and well drained, or will it be flooded if the lake level rises?

4. What is the access to the land? Will existing bridges into the area from nearby towns hold trucks which might later come with building materials, if cabins or other structures would be built? Are the roads passable in wet weather?

5. Is there a water supply? Ordinarily, satisfactory wells can be drilled along any lake or river but check with the county agent, land commissioner, or local well driller, to be sure.

6. What is the type of vegetation? Trees are nice to have. Poison oak and poison ivy are not so jolly. When I say "poison oak" my wife automatically breaks out in a rash. There is a limit to how much undesirable vegetation you can stand (having had poison ivy twice from head to foot I am perhaps sensitive on the matter, but so are a lot of other people). Some of this undesirable vegetation will tend to come back year after year even if you think you have cleared it all. But a few choice trees can be invaluable in selling an acreage—they give "atmosphere."

7. Are slopes excessive and subject to erosion? *There is a fine line, sometimes, between view property and landslide property.* Would road-building and maintenance be a problem?

8. Are utilities available, potentially? (REA, etc.). This may or may not be a big advantage. Some people prefer things rustic.

9. What sort of fishing does the body of water offer? Check with the state game and fish commission; almost all lakes have been surveyed in considerable

detail. The State of Minnesota puts out excellent
maps of many lakes showing depth of lake, nature
of shoreline, and types of vegetation along the
shore. They also have reports on studies they have
made of the fish populations. Other states have
similar maps and studies available free or at very
small cost. Much more information of this kind is
available than is generally realized.

10. What are the taxes? This is very important and in
some areas it is almost the deciding factor. Also, a
number of states now provide public access to
many lakes, and the advantage of owning lakeshore
has been somewhat reduced by this circumstance.
When abundant public access is combined with
high taxes on even undeveloped land (and these
circumstances definitely exist right now in some
areas), lakeshore may be a less desirable investment
than many other things. Lakeshore may provide
many things for you that money cannot buy, but at
some point costs of owning lakeshore may take the
joy out of the situation. Taxes have to be reasonable if you are going to invest in a property and
develop it over a period of years.

11. Is the property adjacent to public lands? Much
waterfrontage and other private tracts adjoin large
areas of the public domain (U. S. Forest Service
lands, or State Forest lands). This circumstance
usually counts as a strong plus factor for the land
because you have the use of the adjacent public
land free, ordinarily. Also, you will have good fire
protection for your property, for any fire on your
land will be regarded as a threat to the public lands
and promptly fought. If a forest lookout spots a

lightning-struck tree on fire in the area of his forest, he will go over and put it out whether it happens to be on your land or not.

12. How far can you travel by water from your land? Some lake and river systems allow you to go for many miles, and somebody sitting in a city with a big boat in his backyard may be just the man who wants to buy a piece of land from you so he will have a place to launch and moor his boat and build a small cabin. In general, land on a large body of water commands a better price than that located on smaller water areas.

See the property firsthand.

Numerous other suggestions in evaluating lakeshore and river frontage could be made, but these are some of the principal considerations. If the country has marked seasons (winter and summer) it is well to visit the area during each of these times. You can see a lot more when the leaves have fallen. But in any case, by all means do go and see the property before you buy. One view is worth a thousand words, or thousands of dollars if you make a bad blind purchase. I will admit that in my own case I have purchased a couple of tracts of land by seeing them only on air photos and on topographic maps. These investments worked out well but I knew the general area to start with and I am familiar with topographic maps and air photos. If you have someone—a geologist, civil engineer or forester—who is experienced in reading maps and interpreting air photos with whom to consult, you might consider this approach if you have no alternatives. But a visit on the spot is still by far the best.

Private land surrounded by public land.

Some private lakeshore tracts (as well as lands with no
waterfront) are now completely surrounded by public lands.
This is true, for example, of certain remote parcels in the
Superior National Forest of northern Minnesota. In such
circumstances, access may be a problem but occasionally
there is a reasonably good solution—trade property with the
Government. The Forest Service or other governmental
agency involved sometimes is willing to trade a piece of their
land on the edge of the public tract for the piece of private
land surrounded by the public land. In this way they "block
out" their acreages. Before buying such a piece of "land-
locked" acreage, however, you should check in detail to see
if such a trade is possible and if it would be worthwhile.

Some details of waterfront development.

This book is basically written for the small investor. If
you are a large investor you will lay things out on a grand
scale, hire people and equipment to clear the land for you,
with not too much personal physical effort, on your part,
involved. But as a small investor you may want to do most
of the work yourself, and maybe even get the family involved
in it. It actually doesn't take much equipment. A small bulldozer hired locally is about as large a piece of machinery
you might use. If you hire such a machine and operator, be
sure you know exactly what you want to have done before
you start—have things carefully staked out. Even small bull-

dozers eat up money fast, but if used efficiently they can do a tremendous amount of work in a short time.

My equipment has consisted of an old station wagon, a chain saw (second hand), a couple of axes and hand saws, a shovel, a rake, and a power mower. I obtain or myself draw a good map of the property, enlarge it if necessary, lay out plans for roads through the place, and then go to work putting in the roads and making the clearings. Here and there you may need to put in a culvert (get concrete or steel pipes from the local lumber yard or concrete plant). Sometimes just a load or two of gravel will do wonders for a soft spot in the road and also influence your rural neighbors the right way because you spent the money for the gravel with them. (Buying your supplies locally as much as possible really pays off in neighbor goodwill, and information.)

Once you have your acreage worked up in good shape, you may want to invite out a local real estate agent to talk with him about it. He will usually make some good suggestions as to what details might be added to make the land more salable.

It doesn't increase your taxes to have a surveyor come out and survey the land and plat it into smaller parcels, but once you file that plat with the county commissioner (or to whomever it goes) then you are in the real estate business more or less and the assessor is quite likely to come out and reappraise things, and your taxes will go up. It is important not to make such a move until you are ready to sell. Lining up a few potential buyers in advance is a good precaution.

How long you want to hold the land before you divide it up and sell it is, of course, a personal matter. Given reasonable taxes, you can hold it for years, work on it from time to time, enjoy it, and know that you are holding one of the very best investments. As already stated in this chapter, recreational land, especially waterfrontage, is one of the most satisfying forms of investment ventures in which you can engage. For me it has been both fun and profitable, and I put the importance of those two things in that order.

Other recreational land.

Many farm lands are marginal. This has been one of the biggest national headaches we have had, and is in part the reason for many of our various, and in some cases seemingly absurd, farm programs. But to the marginal farmer, these programs have frequently helped him bridge the gap from staying on the farm to selling the farm and moving to the city—and this has been going on for a long time.

What happens to marginal farms?

This has been a question of national concern; perhaps you can provide a profitable solution in some cases. Other people have thought about specific farms and come up with some good answers.

What can be done with an abandoned farm out in the foothills, or with acreage on the edge of a forest, or with swampy land, or with poor land near a large city?

Here are some possibilities:

Golf course, or driving range.
Picnic grounds and amusement park.
Car and motorcycle racetrack.
Riding stables and trails.
Christmas tree farm where city people can come out
    and cut their own trees.
Roller skating rink in a rustic setting.
Ski-lift, or "view-lift" site, if area has a high hill.

"Country-style restaurant"—convert the old farm-house.

Summer home sites.

Gun club.

You can no doubt think of many other possibilities depending on local needs and tastes.

At the moment, of course, we have much more marginal land than we need for golf courses or what have you, so the number of marginal acres ripe for development at any one time is limited. But as cities sprawl out, highways are improved, and new highways and freeways built, the scene constantly changes. What may just be rolling brush hills one day may be somebody's country club the next. We have all seen new enterprises develop in unexpected places. Yet when they are put in, however, it suddenly seems obvious that this was the right time and the right place. A year ago we never thought of it. Nobody else did either, probably, except one man. Look over the area you live in, and give your imagination some free rein. Don't get carried away, be realistic, but remember that everything built started as an idea in someone's mind.

New roads open new areas.

One basic factor in connection with the development of rural marginal lands, of course, is the ability of people to get easily and quickly to the area. Here a little research may pay big dividends in the form of ideas as to what areas are going to shortly come into popularity. Traveling in California will give you an insight into what will no doubt happen in other areas soon. In California, thousands of people from

Los Angeles travel 400 miles over a weekend to ski or hike in the mountains. In the Midwest such a trip is still the exception. However, freeways are cutting through the maze of our older cities in the East and Midwest and 400 miles is not now the distance it once was, when the highway went down the main street of every little town and the merchants put up as many stop signs as possible to get a few customers.

Lands regarded only a few years ago as relatively remote are now close at hand, thanks to the freeways. More and more we tend to measure distances not in miles, but in terms of time. Regardless of the mileage, the fundamental thing is "It is only 2 hours now to Birch Lake."

Our superhighways are opening large new areas for development. I was amazed on a recent trip to California to see the number and quality of summer homes (and used in the winter too, as ski huts) which are being built in increasing numbers in distant parts of the Sierra Nevada. The same is true in the hinterland west of Denver.

To illustrate that this is not all theory, let me quote an ad which appeared recently in *The Wall Street Journal*.

SKI ACREAGE

Wanted by listed California Corporation for investment portfolio. The parcel should be well located and realistically offered. It must have highway frontage.

(followed by address at end of ad)

What was one day strictly marginal land, and a hillside at that, probably too steep and too far out of town for any residential development, probably became a first class ski resort the next.

RESIDENTIAL LAND

According to Franz Pick, noted expert on finance and economics, the best investments in 1965 in terms of price appreciation were in unimproved land on the outskirts of cities. Gains far outran the 11% rise in the Dow-Jones Industrial stock average.

The old rule was "Start walking out of town on the main street. When they quote you land prices by the acre instead of by the front foot, buy." The rule still generally applies, but taxes and city planning, county zoning, utility districts and water districts, and many more things have made the problem of what and where to buy a little more difficult.

Some people suggest that our cities will not grow so fast in the future as they have in the past—that they tend to choke themselves to death. As a country boy who has on occasion been lost in the wilds of New York, Chicago, and Los Angeles, I am inclined to agree. But the fact is, the availability of utilities, of medical and other services, and of cultural centers (libraries, concert halls, schools, et cetera), depends on having a reasonably dense population, and we will have cities for a long time to come. But they may not be cities quite as we know them today. They may become less centralized and more elongated—"strip cities" they are being called. In any event, land around metropolitan areas is going to be used, and it is being used faster and faster. Strip cities are with us today, and the locations of future strip cities are relatively obvious: Seattle-Portland-Eugene, Minneapolis-St. Paul-Duluth, the east and west coasts of Florida, to name just a few.

The wise purchase of potential residential (subdivision) land is an art which is itself the subject of entire books; but perhaps the viewpoint of a geologist may bring out some factors which you may not have considered.

Factors in direction of city growth.

Topography—the shape of the land—is a strong growth direction control, of course. Chicago, Milwaukee, Cleveland, and Buffalo, for example, are bordered on one side by a lake. San Francisco, Seattle, Miami, and New York have salt water borders in part. Denver and Salt Lake City have tremendous mountain ranges behind them. In these cases, adding 100,000 people does not mean simply drawing an additional circle representing this many persons around the city. It means a directional projection of growth. Sometimes this direction is rather a limited one with a corresponding rapid development in that direction. But even communities in relatively flat areas with no strong control by a body of water or a mountain range, will show a directional growth trend. This is noticeable to varying degrees when flying over the Great Plains area. In general, towns and cities in North America, other things being equal, tend to grow in a southwesterly direction. The reason for this, I am told, is that the prevailing winds are from the southwest and dust and industrial fumes are blown northeastward. The more desirable residential locations are windward—to the southwest and away from the fumes, dirt and noises of the city, toward the fresh air and open country-side.

This principle, of course, is subject to modifications, one being where the water supply is and how the city mains are laid out. Water, however, can be carried relatively easily to outlying areas, but sewers are another matter. Most subdivisions outside a city will have city water piped to them quite quickly if not initially, but city sewer connections usually come much later. Therefore, give due consideration to whether or not that piece of acreage you want to buy will be approved for septic tanks on a 10,000 square foot lot (which is a good average sized lot in most areas). How do you find out? Go usually to the county health department. They will have a strong opinion (and usually authority) on the septic tank situation. They can give you an opinion based on general drainage characteristics of the area and from tests they have made or will make on soil percolation.

"Mantle" is the loose material on the Earth's surface above the "bedrock." Bedrock is where the digging gets tough. In some places the solid rock lies deep, and roads, foundations, sewers, and water lines can be put in with no trouble, but if the solid rock is only a few inches below the surface, watch out. The cost of water lines, sewer lines, or septic tanks in solid rock is many times that of putting them through nice soft sand or clay. It will definitely pay you to dig a hole, or auger a hole down a couple of feet at least, *in several places* (the highest and lowest points for sure; the highest because that is where the mantle is likely to be the thinnest and the bedrock sticks out, and the lowest because you can see how close the water stands to the surface and how severe your drainage problems for septic tanks might be).

Does the area flood? Usually it can't get too dry, assuming you have some sort of water supply, but it surely can get too wet. I was in Oregon during the floods of Christmas, 1964, when they had to open the drawbridge on the Umpqua River to let a house and two barns float out to sea! Whom do you ask about this? Don't take the owner's word for it, or that of the real estate agent anxious to make a sale. Go ask the county engineer's office; if it is cropland, ask the county agent. You pay taxes to support these services; make use of them. It has amazed me to see how rarely people investing large amounts of money take time to thoroughly check the various aspects of their proposed purchases. A lot more information is available than is generally known. *Take the time to get information.*

Timing all-important—when do major price rises occur?

A tract of land in Mendocino County, north of San Francisco, sold for $22.50 an acre in 1957. In 1965 it was selling for $2,200 an acre! How long was the price $22.50 an acre or less?—from the beginning of time until shortly after 1957. Then look what happened in just a few years! Land will lie near a town for years and be just farm land, but eventually there comes a time when it begins to obviously look as if it will soon be residential land. I had a piece of land one time which I offered for sale for several years without the appearance of a single interested buyer. Then, one year it seemed that everybody wanted to buy it. I sold it, and in following it along afterward found that it more than doubled in price again in just 3 years. After that it leveled off. There is about a 3 to 5 year period more or less when land will move up in price several times as fast as it has been doing for the past 20 years or more. Once the price has moved up to the level of subdivided residential property, in effect, whether it is subdivided or not, this price rise curve will flatten out. At this point, however, the tax assessor will be around and the tax curve will begin to rise rapidly and the property then should be sold fairly fast and developed into individual homesites or your profit will be severely eroded by taxes.

Good reason to begin your investments near home.

You can make your money work much harder for you if you know a situation well enough to anticipate just when this jump in value will take place, and buy accordingly. This is why you should begin your real estate ventures near home —*where you know the situation best.*

Develop small tracts in your area.

Often it is possible, through your own efforts, to cause a piece of raw acreage to move up rapidly in value within a short time. Select a few acres with access and other basic factors in its favor (principal one being you can drill a well and get water). Then go to work.

As an example, and by no means an unusual one, I can cite a chap who bought 15 acres of cut-over timber land near his town for $5,000, paying only a little down. He bought a second-hand chain saw for $75. He roughly surveyed the land with a compass and a 100-foot tape, and made a sketch map and a development plan. He cut a series of roads through the area, and in the process cut a three-year supply of firewood for himself from the scrub second growth of trees on the place. This he gradually hauled home each weekend in his station wagon as he made trips to and from his acreage. The acreage happened to be on a small hill, and he cleared several sites which had exceptionally nice views, seeded a little grass in these clearings, mowed them, and produced some very attractive lawn-like areas. He trimmed up the trees, cut the underbrush, collected the downed branches and burned them. After a year the place looked like a park. One sunny spring day he ran an ad in the local paper. The first couple who drove out to see the place, parked in one of these pretty grassy clearings, took in the view that had been provided by cutting a few trees, and promptly bought the place for $11,000. The acreage was well worth the price, and the family that bought the land is the envy of all their friends. The man who developed the acreage combined imagination, enthusiasm, and his own efforts to create this situation, and make some money. It was a good deal for everyone.

Except for the details, this story applies to several individuals I know—each with a little enterprise plus some vision—who got some good exercise and a lot of fun out of developing small acreages right around the towns in which they live. One school teacher of my acquaintance has been doing this for several years—buying cheap land, and putting a lot of his own effort into these areas. He has had more time than money, using part of his three months off from his junior high school job to work in this fashion, as well as using occasional weekends during the school year. Now he has several tracts which, when sold, will make him virtually financially independent. Another fellow I know had invested in a little acreage, fortunately paying cash for it so he didn't have any payments to make, who then, through no fault of his own, lost his job. While he was looking for another job, he put in some of his time working on the acreage, finally fixed it beautifully and sold it. He later calculated that while he was out of work, but working on his acreage, he had been making $18 an hour! His efforts on the acreage had boosted its value so he eventually sold it for twice what he had paid for it. And his "wages" were taxed at long term capital gains rates!

Simple facts and figures.

Here are a few suggestions, facts, and figures related to developing land: Buy a 100-foot steel tape measure. With it determine how much of the land is actually usable for its highest purpose (presumably this usually would be as a home site), and how much, because of ravines, swamps, rocks, et cetera, is not usable, or of inferior quality. Make these calculations *before* you buy, and make your offer accordingly. There are 43,560 square feet in an acre. An acre is roughly 200 by 220 feet. One acre will readily divide into 3 nice city lots (about 10,000 square feet each) with enough left over to take care of streets and sidewalks. Four lots to the acre is squeezing things a bit, especially if septic tanks are involved for the sewage system. Check this matter of septic tank permits with the county health department, as has already been suggested (but it is worth saying again). Always, always check on easements which may be on the property. An easement is usually permanent and means that somebody else has the use of part of the land for a water line, a road, a power line, or something of the sort. If you intend to sell the property to someone planning to put up a large building, the existence and exact location of easements is all-important. You may find, when you have mapped the positions of the easements, that there is a lot less usable land than you thought, and for some sorts of buildings the property may not be suitable at all, if easements cut up the area so that the individual easement-free parcels are not of proper size or shape. The title to the property will ordinarily have the easements recorded, but not always. Be sure to ask about them.

You get slightly more land if you buy sloping land than if you buy flat acreage. Land area is figured on the basis of a flat surface; therefore, an acre of sloping land contains more than an acre of land surface. This is a minor factor, but where land prices are high it might be given some slight consideration. The asset this might be, however, must be balanced against road-building and other problems which arise when land is sloping steeply. But on the other hand, frequently you have "view property" with sloping land, which is a plus-factor, and you can charge accordingly. So balance these items carefully. Each situation is different and each presents a challenge—and perhaps an opportunity.

Don't buy landslides.

In the case of hillside property, be very sure you aren't buying into a landslide. Landslides leave big and little scars (dish-shaped or spoon-shaped marks on the hill) which you can readily identify with a little practice. Nevertheless, I have recently seen some severely landslide-scarred property sold and it now has a number of new houses on it. Regulations on building sites should definitely be strengthened. California has come a long way in this regard, and other states would do well to follow suit. If you are considering a hillside, look it over carefully, and if you know a geologist or engineer, ask him for an opinion on it. If you want to see construction, and problems which developed on an excellent example of landslide topography, go see where the city of Portland, Oregon, built its zoo.

Conclusions.

The development of residential land sites in almost any area can be both a pleasant and a profitable spare-time activity. If a few simple precautions are followed in choosing the land, it is difficult to see how you could lose much money in such a venture, and the return on your investment and your efforts could be very large.

INDUSTRIAL AND COMMERCIAL LAND

It has been my observation that both speculation and investment in industrial and commercial land involve so many factors and also, commonly, such large amounts of money that the average investor generally will not find this field as easy to operate in or understand, as some other areas of land investment. Nevertheless, possibilities do exist, and it is interesting to note that some firms are "stockpiling" industrial sites they really have no use for at the moment, because the ultimate demand will be very great. As a side effect of this, some companies already find that land has been one of their better investments—better than money placed in their own operations at times. Chemway Corporation assembled a 230-acre site and then because of a proposed freeway, decided to sell some. Prices they received for the land were up to four times what they had paid a few years earlier.

Light industries need smaller sites.

Sizes of industrial sites differ markedly. A steel company recently bought 800 acres in Illinois, whereas a small electronics firm purchased 20 acres not far from where I live. Detailed requirements of various companies differ so much that it is hard to predict in advance just what sort of company would fit a given situation (by comparison, housing developments are relatively standard in the size of lots, and their needs—water, light, perhaps sewers—are readily determinable). Some companies need abundant water supplies for their processes. Some need very little water except for the drinking fountains and sanitary needs. Requirements as to labor supply differ too. Some industries depend on all-male highly trained people; some companies need the sort of help afforded by housewives in a suburban community. Some companies need easy access to a railroad; others couldn't care less about rail access, preferring to ship everything by truck.

Talk to a real estate specialist.

Some real estate men specialize in industrial property, and my advice is to talk with these men if you are interested in this sort of investment, or if you own property which you think might make a good industrial site. If you can sell your land this way, you can sometimes do very nicely, for a company will pay well for an acreage they think is choice for their purposes. It should be noted, also, that some companies may prefer to take long leases on land rather than buy land, and this may offer the investor a chance to obtain an excellent income from his property but still allow him to retain it for long term capital gains, and as an inflation hedge.

Industrial parks.

One aspect of industrial land trends today deserves special mention here—that of the development of so-called "industrial parks." These areas tend to cater to light, smokeless industry. Commonly the people employed are fairly well educated and like to work and live in suburban areas, or even out in the country. Small engineering firms and electronics firms are examples. These industrial parks may grow up well away from any other development. If they are successful they form a nucleus for growth which can be a profitable circumstance to the land investor. These industrial parks provide one instance of how what is farm land one day—farm land which may be well out in the country—can be prime industrial and residential property the next. This field of investment is so specialized, however, that it is hard to fully describe all the circumstances which go into determining a likely spot for an industrial park. By joining the local Chamber of Commerce or talking with them, you can sometimes get ideas; or again, talk with brokers who may know about such trends and who specialize in industrial types of land.

Commercial land.

This category includes such things as sites for restaurants, motels, filling stations, shopping centers, et cetera. In general, the prime requisite is to have the property located where lots of people pass every day, and who pass in such a way as to have access to the property. Many of our roads and all of our freeways have "restricted access" or "limited access." (You have seen such signs along the highways—"Restricted access for next 42 miles." This means you can't put a culvert across the roadside ditch just any place and thus join your property to the highway because having such access would be a hazard on a high speed highway.)

In cities, of course, access is generally available to all property but most heavy traffic sites in cities have already been identified and built on, or if not already built up are well up in price.

The larger profits are to be made in areas where a new road goes through; and with our tremendous nation-wide road building program, opportunities are many. I recall one such area on the West Coast which I passed frequently during a summer while I was geologically mapping the region for an oil company. It was a fairly level piece of land but with poor soil, good chiefly for grazing, and cows in the field watched me drive by day after day. In one corner of the field there was a rather weathered "For Sale" sign, and I surely could see no reason why anybody would want to buy this particular acreage. It was pasture land and nothing more— until a freeway was projected through the area and a clover-leaf interchange was built in the middle of the field. The farm land, which I later found out had been offered for sale via the weathered sign for $125 an acre, was purchased by various concerns including an oil company and a supermarket, for prices ranging up to $6,000 an acre. This rise in value from the time I saw it first at $125 an acre to its $6,000 per acre selling price took place in less than 6 years.

Here again you can probably do best right in your own community, for you will become aware of the need for new roads earlier than outsiders would, you will know the land situation, and you can, with little study, see where interchanges are likely to be built. The very rapid growth of our population, and particularly the development of "strip cities," provide numerous investment opportunities, and there is no early end in sight for this trend.

FARM LAND

The urge to own a piece of land is probably most frequently expressed in each of us by the vague thought that we should buy a farm so we could always retire there, if necessary, and raise a few things. Whereas I would like to preserve this fond thought for all of us, I am duty bound to say what I think—or in this case tell you what I know from a considerable amount of experience. I never retired to a farm, and I don't think I ever will; but I owned a farm and farmed it in various ways for more than 10 years.

Our politicians still cater to the nostalgic ideal that the 80 acre farm homestead is the backbone of American life, and expresses the "American Way." By and large, the fact is the 80 acre farm is uneconomic and that is why people have been leaving it and moving to the city in droves.

Farming for the most part is big business and it is getting bigger. Drive across the Dakotas, Kansas, Nebraska, or Oklahoma and many similar areas and see the old farm houses falling into ruin. Where are these people who run the farms? They are in some city, usually nearby, enjoying the advantages of city living (closeness to schools, medical facilities, shopping centers, cultural and sports events), and they drive out to the farm to work it just as somebody else goes to the office.

Farming has faced a cost squeeze for years, and smaller farms have been combined into larger ones for the most part. It takes machinery to farm economically and it takes a lot of land to justify the cost of the machinery you need.

I can tell you all about the joys of an 80 acre farm (mine was 85 acres)—how the year I decided to plant barley the price of barley went to a recent new low. Then I decided to plant English rye grass, and the blight got the crop that year. I can tell you how borrowed machinery breaks down, and your rental time is mostly taken up with repairs. I finally rented out the acreage to a good reliable farmer who, instead of moving to the city as most of his neighbors did, decided to stay in the farming business; and because he had more machinery and better machinery than anybody else locally, he rented other farms and finally put together a total of 800 acres (including my 85) and now is able to efficiently use his equipment. You can't have a combine, a tractor, three different kinds of plows and discs, and some drags to handle just 85 acres. But you must have this equipment to farm and stay in business. So there is the problem—all too well known to small farmers.

Certain special situations do occasionally occur where small farm tracts may be profitable; if the price of the land is low enough when you buy it, your investment return can be good. These situations are rare, but before you skip on to greener investment pastures, pause; there are some bright spots in the farm investment business. Here are some of them, along with the general fact that farming can only get better for it is at low ebb at the moment, and population demands on food are rising rapidly.

Specialty farms.

The preceding experiences relate chiefly to small grain farms. Some specialty farms do very well. In a good year, a potato farm can gross $1,000 and possibly much more than that per acre. I know of one farmer who grossed well over $80,000 on 89 acres of potatoes one year, but this was after several years of making very little. Nevertheless, he has done well enough over the years on approximately an 80 acre situation, to accumulate over a quarter of a million dollars in assets. Grape and orange growers in California do well at the right time and place. The Pacific Northwest has a thriving holly industry. Other people in this region raise walnuts and filberts.

In these specialty crops, with a relatively small amount of acreage involved but high value products being produced, lie opportunities for people, including people thinking of retiring, to have a farm of sorts and make a good to excellent living. My experience and all my inquiries have indicated that in general these ventures do best if the person who owns one operates it also; but in some cases investments can be made on shares with a reliable individual and it is not necessary to manage the place yourself, beyond visiting it occasionally.

The variety of specialty situations is large, and this field of enterprise, for someone wishing to invest in a small farm, is worth considering; for a special or local market may lie waiting to be discovered or developed.

Farms as an investment—advantage and some problems.

There are some very definite, and, in part unique, advantages to farms as investments. Farm land is a hedge against inflation (although taxes wipe out some of this advantage), and it is theft-proof and bomb-proof. Further, it seems likely that the current situation of farm surpluses may gradually disappear. Much of the world goes to bed hungry, and we are losing ground on this problem, which is an economic one. If education and technology allow people of the world to earn enough to eat well, and trade channels are open so they can sell their goods and buy food, our crop surpluses will vanish. Last year the Food and Agriculture Organization of the United Nations reported that agricultural output did not keep pace with population growth, and for the previous 5 years it only kept even. Food will not go out of style, and demand is surely rising.

How about putting your farm in the Soil Bank? We have all heard stories about how certain people have purchased farms (chiefly marginal ones) and then put them in the Soil Bank or some other Government program and made large profits. This sort of thing no doubt occurred as various subsidy plans and other devices got started; but those days are over, for the most part. One reason that the yield on farm land investment is so low today is that the price of land has gone up based on the fact that these Government schemes have been in existence at various times, and people think they will be instituted again. Many of these programs were designed to help the farmer on marginal land, after World War II, make the adjustment from farming to doing something else. Most of these programs have been or are being phased out. Furthermore, each new Congress has its own ideas of what should be done about the farm problem; and when you buy a farm you buy into this problem, for better or for worse. Predicting what Congress is going to do is worthy of the judgment of Solomon, and I would hesitate to base my investments on such shifting sand. If you buy a marginal farm and convert it to a summer resort or a golf course, that is something else again. Here marginal farms can in some cases be very worthwhile investments; but this matter belongs under the topic of recreational land and has already been discussed there (see chapter on WATER-FRONT AND OTHER RECREATIONAL LAND).

Farm land yields.

If you invest in a farm, what can you expect in the way of return? I have talked with many farm real estate dealers, with officials in various Government agencies—chiefly those of the Agriculture Department—and with bankers in farm areas who *know* how farmers are doing. Even in relatively good farm areas such as in eastern Kansas and southern Minnesota, rate of return is commonly as low as 5% net. My own farm averaged 4%. Locally, unusually fertile farm land plus efficient farming produce a 10% or better net yield, but this is exceptional.

As an investment for income, farms generally have been just fair—about like the yield on common stocks, but with many more headaches, and this comparison is worth a few words. If you buy stock in a company you get good management (usually). You don't have to worry about the details of the business yourself. This is not so with farm land. Even if you rent it out, you still have to first get a good renter, and good ones are the exception. They may move away or be taken ill at a critical time in the planting or harvesting season. In fact, buying a farm can involve you in all sorts of problems you never expected, such as the case of one farmer who worked a number of farms on lease and whose wife ran off with another man just as the spring planting should have begun. It so shook up the farmer that nothing was done on any of his rented farms—and what could the people do who owned the farms? They hadn't covered that sort of emergency in their agreements with the farmer. And there may be more headaches such as fixing fences to keep the neighbor's sheep out of your alfalfa, putting in drain tile, collecting beer bottles off the edge of your land adjacent to the road, and a hundred other vexations. Also basic to all real estate investments, including farms, is the fact that taxes accumulate whether you are getting an income from the land or not. You have to keep working the land if you are going to just break even, much less get ahead. If you buy stock you usually don't have to pay any tax on it if it doesn't give you any dividends. (Some states such as Florida, however, do have a small tax on securities held.) I don't know all the problems in farming but I know enough to make this chapter book-length in itself.

Demand for land—a strong plus-factor.

One thing should be added, however. Farming for current income has serious drawbacks for the small investor.

But if you are willing to get along with a modest return, farm lands if chosen with any reasonable degree of care do offer a good capital gains potential, for farm land prices have been going up faster even than the rate of inflation. Even just fair farm land will probably not go down in value, which is more than can be said for many stocks you might buy today. All indications are that this trend will continue, perhaps at an even faster rate than previously. This is true of natural resource investments in general, and is one of the chief appeals this sort of thing has as a place to put your money, and why people are increasingly attracted to natural resource investments. Land investments even have a small psychological aspect in their favor—farm land has a sturdy look about it which paper stock certificates, in spite of all the fancy engraving, don't necessarily possess in the eyes of some people. There definitely is appeal in being able to go out and look at your investment, and walk around on it. It gives one the feeling of being involved in a solid situation, when you walk over a piece of the Earth which you own; and this feeling is not an illusion. Land is basic, with much in its favor as an investment.

Probable reversal of depressed farming situation.

A full page ad in a recent *Wall Street Journal* was head-lined "FAMINE STALKS THE EARTH." The statistics to back up this grim statement are shockingly more evident every day. Right now more than half of the wheat, soybeans, dried peas, and milled rice produced in the United States ends up abroad. There is strong evidence too that the U. S. Government, right now, is in the process of going from a policy of discouraging farm production to encouraging production. Most of our food surpluses are all but gone. I believe we are seeing the beginning of a new era for farmers, and farm land will definitely be in greater demand the next few years than it has been for the past 15 or so.

Summary.

Farming, in general, is big business; some specialty farms pay off for the small investor, usually best if he runs them himself. Farm land can be bought and rented out but the rate of return is small and the headaches can be considerable. However, the overall world food shortage, currently getting worse instead of better, will probably eliminate our crop surpluses before too long. Our depressed farming situation may be in for a fundamental change for the better. As a long term investment for capital gains, farm land is good, perhaps even excellent, in some situations. Demand for land absolutely cannot decrease; as demand goes up and up for something that is definitely in fixed supply such as land is, there can be only one result—the value will go up. There is no foreseeable reversal to this trend.

Investing in land is an endeavor where the long term odds are decidedly in your favor if you use a few relatively simple guidelines in your choice of land. Some of these guidelines have been set forth in the preceding pages.

Timber and Trees

This form of investment can take either of two approaches—raise the timber or other trees yourself, or buy into companies which do. We will look at both possibilities.

First, how about raising timber and trees yourself? By timber I mean trees for lumber; by trees I mean specialty trees such as ornamental trees of various sorts (junipers, blue spruce, flowering trees, et cetera).

TREE FARMING

Trees live a long time—many of them live longer than do people. If you think of raising trees in the Pacific Northwest you are talking chiefly about ponderosa pine and Douglas fir—and you are talking in terms of 40 to 80 years for a crop. You can buy into partially grown tree situations where the time to maturity is less; but remember you are still talking about years—usually many years. For most small investors this may lack appeal. Also, managing a tree farm takes a lot of work. Fire, disease, or insects are hazards which may in a few minutes, or during one summer, wipe out the accumulated value and effort of many years. It can be a very discouraging business for an individual. A corporation can take a fifty-year view; it can spread its risks and work on the law of averages. Most individual investors don't have the time or the money to do this.

Tree farming in the South.

In the Southern states, however, the southern yellow pine, and certain other species, grow fast, and the local view of what is commercial timber in terms of the size of the tree is vastly different from in the Pacific Northwest. What is a toothpick in western Oregon is a salable tree in Mississippi or Arkansas. In the South, I am told, commercial timber can be raised in as short a time as 15 to 20 years. This situation may be attractive for the small investor. If you plan far enough ahead you could buy a piece of land, plant a forest some years before you retire, and then, by the time you are ready to retire, you may have an acreage which, through selective logging, can keep you profitably and pleasantly busy. This has been done and is being done. Also, land in the South is rising in price in some places more rapidly even than land in other parts of the country; and tree farms can provide a good hedge against inflation just from the matter of the land involved. Anything gotten off of it in the form of timber is pure gravy. Taxes also, I find, are generally somewhat more reasonable on southern land than on much northern and western land.

Tree farming in the Midwest and Pacific Northwest.

The South is the place the small investor should look first at the tree farming possibilities. The Pacific Northwest, as we have seen, is, by and large, a situation for corporations which can take the long view. In the northern Midwest (Minnesota, Wisconsin, Michigan), in the New England states, and down through the Appalachians, some possibilities for the small investor exist. I think the best possibilities are those which involve combining the raising of trees with other things—chiefly recreational developments. This is the well-known "multiple use" concept which the Federal Government is pursuing with many of its forest lands.

I have owned timberland for a number of years in Minnesota, and can report it is a marginal proposition so far as I have found. The timber is slow growing, and taxes relatively high, although in places it is possible to make arrangements for special tax treatment of timberland. I compared my results with those of a prominent timber and paper company. Their chief forester was most helpful, and he stated that on lands which cost the company $8 to $10 an acre, the yield, after taxes and management, ran between 25 cents and 50 cents an acre annually—more generally toward the lower figure. You can probably do this well with your money in a bank or savings and loan association, without the worry about fire or vandalism or a dozen other problems. However, if you have an area which is especially fertile, and there is good road access to your timber holdings, and a good local market exists for the crop (a high grade paper company, perhaps), you may be able to get a fair return on your money. I have timberland only because it also happens to be lakeshore property. This combination is a happy one; the timber gives a long term growth factor to the investment, and the lakeshore is increasing in value more rapidly. I recommend this combination highly, and in reviewing in my mind all the individuals I know who have made this sort of investment I cannot recall anyone who ever lost money —in most cases it has been quite the contrary. And such situations definitely can still be found (see chapter on WATERFRONT AND OTHER RECREATIONAL LAND).

SPECIALTY TREES

Specialty trees are tree farming on a small scale with a high unit-value product; but here I am hard pressed to decide whether or not I am really talking about natural resources in the strict sense. What we are discussing actually is going into the tree nursery business, which does have possibilities for the small investor. My father is a licensed nurseryman in Minnesota, and has raised fancy trees as a hobby for many years. He has gotten a great deal of enjoyment from it, and if my wanderings as a geologist eventually become restricted enough to allow me to stay home during a substantial part of any summer, I would like to take up this business myself, on a small scale.

I do know enough about the specialty tree business to state that it involves a lot of hard work, is very competitive, and again, like any tree business, it takes time. In the case of specialty trees, however, the time for a crop to mature is shorter, of course, than in the case of timber. There is a wonderful variety of ornamental trees; usually the market for these is best in an area where the suburbs are growing fast with lots of new landscaping going on.

A friend of mine who worked as a geologist with me in

South America and lived next door to me there for a time, had a "green thumb." I remember him well as he occasionally would have a load of goat manure dumped in his front yard to aid his gardening activities. It is rather powdery stuff when dry, and the strong breezes which blew in from the Pacific Ocean at our doorstep in northern Peru, would blow some of this fertilizer around and impart a very (to say the least) distinctive flavor to my poached eggs in the morning. This chap finally quit geology and moved to California where he opened a nursery and landscaping service. He has done exceedingly well, but he tells me the first few years were very lean while he was developing his stock of trees and shrubs.

Summary.

Tree farming in the South is attractive to the small investor; in the North it tends to be marginal, but can be combined with recreational lands with exceptional long term profit possibilities; in the West, tree farming is probably for the big corporations which can take the longer view. Specialty trees, however, are a shorter term proposition, offering small scale possibilities which are suitable for the individual.

TIMBER COMPANIES

What about investing in timber companies? I think any substantial stock portfolio should have this industry represented. There are vast areas of the United States and Canada which are best suited chiefly for growing timber and pulpwood. As a continent we are most generously endowed with this resource. It offers an excellent investment medium for both the large and small investor through the many companies engaged in this industry.

Wood is a very versatile material, and new uses are being found for it every day. (Just the billions of forms the Government insists we fill out should insure the future of the paper industry!) Wood chemistry has a very good future, as there is virtually no limit to the number of different substances which can be constructed from hydrocarbon raw materials, such as wood cellulose. One interesting example is the production of food from wood. Vanillin is made from wood, and is a synthetic vanilla flavoring which costs much less on the grocery store shelf than does the real thing. Also, some cattle are now eating molasses produced from wood sugars. The syrup, called Masonex, is made as a by-product from the manufacture of hardboard panels by Masonite Corporation.

Not only do new products make for a good growth trend in the timber industry, but my first hand observations over several years on the way logging is conducted in some areas and the amount of wood which is left to rot, suggest to me that we are still very inefficient in this business compared with similar operations in certain other parts of the world, and that a great increase in productivity can be obtained as research on this problem continues. Profit margins for aggressive companies can widen accordingly.

Hidden values.

In considering investment in timber companies, one should investigate as best one can just how the timber reserves are carried on the company's books. I have spent a number of years in remote areas of the Pacific Northwest, at one time mapping all of western Washington for an oil company, and I was amazed at the tremendous stands of timber which still exist in both public and private lands. I was interested to note later that, in some cases, the values of timber holdings of the various companies were not fully shown in company reports. Let me clearly state there was no attempt to falsify the reports, but large timber reserves were carried at a very nominal figure in some instances. Perhaps there was no access to the timber at the moment; perhaps the timber had been cruised a number of years before and substantial growth had taken place in the interim. In any case it apparently was just good accounting practice to state values conservatively. But if you have a figure in the company report of the number of board feet approximately in a given timber reserve, it is an easy matter to find out what the price of this is (ask the local U. S. Forest Service office), and make the calculations. By comparing one company with another on a uniform accounting basis you can get an idea of relative values anyway. I do believe I have seen enough of various timberlands to know that there are likely to be hidden values in the stocks of some companies.

Mineral rights may be an unexpected asset.

A further value which may be hidden in stocks of some timber companies is that certain firms own their timberland in fee,[1] including the mineral rights. (Other companies may

---

[1] This is a legal term used in connection with real estate. Sometimes the term is "fee simple" but the meaning in both cases is the same, and refers to complete ownership of a property in every respect, allowing the owner to use it in any way he sees fit, except that it may not become a public nuisance.

own only the surface rights, or in some cases only the cutting rights.) In one area, there was quite a flurry in the price of the stock of one timber company which had extensive holdings near an oil discovery (which I happened to be scouting at the time). Somewhat sadly the timber company finally announced that they only owned the surface rights. The mineral rights were still owned by a railroad which had gotten the land originally by land grant.

In Alaska, Georgia-Pacific Corporation has cutting rights to 8 billion board feet of timber, which is quite an asset in itself, but no mineral rights are involved. In other areas G-P owns the land in fee including mineral rights. How these things are carried on the company books seems to differ somewhat and herein lies a fertile field for research. As a geologist, I am naturally inclined to favor the company that owns the land in fee. Other things being equal, there is always the possibility of an important oil or mineral discovery being made. I know of at least one timber company which owns a large amount of land in fee which has been quietly conducting geological exploration work over its lands for several years. I would not be surprised to have the company turn up some substantial mineral deposits.

Timber company may have real estate sidelines to add income.

Not only can timberland offer the speculative potential of a mineral or oil discovery, but the land can be leased for a variety of uses; and this can be a supplementary source of income to the company. Land development and real estate activity in 1964 produced 14% of the gross income of Pope and Talbot, a West Coast lumber company. Weyerhaeuser

Company has converted about 7,000 acres of its western lands in 5 states to summer home sites, lakeshore recreation centers, and even to one ski resort. With increased population and more leisure time, the greatly increased pressures on our wilderness areas are causing timber companies to study such possibilities for their lands. I think the potential is good, and will get better.

Summary.

Investments in timber companies are attractive for several reasons. The companies produce a material which is very versatile, and for which the demand is increasing rapidly. Further, they are working with a renewable natural resource, which makes it somewhat more attractive, perhaps, than a resource which can be exhausted. The land which the company has is valuable not only for growing timber but as real estate in various forms; and the potential of finding important mineral deposits of various sorts always exists. Recreational aspects of privately held timberlands are just beginning to be appreciated and explored. Well chosen timber company stocks are surely prime long term, as well as short term, investments.

Energy

Although we rarely think of it any more, the amount of energy each of us can command is incredible. You may not be impressed, but if an Indian 200 years ago had been hurled through the air from New York to San Francisco at 650 miles an hour, he would have been impressed! And how much energy does it take just to move the 2 tons of steel called your car, with you in it, 5 to 20 miles or more to work and back each day? Or pull that same 2 tons with all the family in it, 200 miles up into the mountains or to the lake or seashore on a weekend?

In my native Minnesota it takes a lot of energy to keep a house warm when it is 20 below outside. It takes energy to toast bread, light lamps, run the TV, vacuum the floor, run the power mower, plow the farm fields, and run all the machines which produce paper, cloth, and thousands of other things.

The amount of energy you command determines your standard of living to a large extent. For nations it determines military power which involves the very survival of a nation. One of the most interesting books I have ever read is *Energy Sources—the Wealth of the World* (McGraw-Hill,

New York). A man from Gulf Oil Corporation and a man from Westinghouse Corporation put their minds together and wrote a fascinating volume (included on the list of suggested reading at the end of this book). Energy indeed produces wealth, and there is no substitute for energy. Energy is one of the prime needs in the world and always will be. Energy demands, as far as we can look ahead or even imagine, will grow and grow and grow. At the moment, about 73% of the energy used in the United States is derived from petroleum and natural gas. The future will bring shifts in our energy sources but one thing is certain—*the future can only bring a demand for more and more energy*. This is one reason why a company such as the Humble Oil and Refining Company, subsidiary of the Standard Oil Company (N. J.), is gradually changing its sign to ENCO—ENergy COmpany. They intend to stay in the energy business whether it is oil or not; and they have a lot of research going on in such things as fuel cells to make sure they do stay in the energy producing field. They could hardly be in a more fundamental business than one which supplies energy.

A very reasonable prediction is that *energy demands in the United States will triple by the year 2000*. Elsewhere in the world, compared with today, the demands may go up 10 times or more. Clearly, energy producing industries are prime and long term growth industries.

Energy the key to other resources.

In considering energy as an investment, remember that energy is the key which unlocks many other resources. Next to land to stand on, air to breathe, and food and water to eat and drink, energy is about the most fundamental resource we have. In fact, the key to producing more food efficiently, the key to good drinking water both now and in the future (and quite possibly the key to breathing clean air) is energy. Energy is needed to plow our fields, and clean our polluted waters. Energy is needed to convert salt water to fresh water, and energy is being used in the form of electric dust catchers to take industrial wastes out of the air. Energy powers our factories, moves trucks to forests and mines to get raw material, blasts holes in the rocks to find our ores, and powers drilling equipment that now probes over 4 miles into the Earth to find oil.

There is no foreseeable limit to the energy needs of the United States and the world. Assuming reasonable Government treatment, energy sources can hardly be anything but prime investments. They are, generally, not highly speculative and subject to wild price rises and drops, for they occupy a well established solid position in our economy. You may strike it rich through a new energy-release process which some small company invents (a break-through on large-scale commercial application of fuel cells would be an example), or some small oil company may find a new oil field and multiply its assets manyfold; but energy producers such as utilities are not likely to double their stock price in a matter of a few months, as an occasional speculative issue in mining may do. However, my firm impression is that 5 utilities or solidly situated oil companies will show a better return over a 10 year period than will 5 pure speculations, on the average. And during these 10 years you will have peace of mind instead of ulcers, and this is a dividend you shouldn't ignore either.

Every investor with any reasonable amount of funds, should have some energy source stocks in his portfolio. Furthermore, I believe energy is such a fundamental and growing field that every investor should try to follow to some degree, at least, new developments in this area. One mutual fund, Energy Fund, Inc., invests almost exclusively in energy stocks; and they make it a point to keep abreast of latest advances and shifts in emphasis in this field. I have a few shares of this fund myself, chiefly because through their reports to stockholders and other information sent out from time to time, I am informed on their thinking on this important investment area. Frequently things are brought to my attention in this manner of which I would not otherwise be aware until later.

Demand for energy can only go up and up. In the following chapters we will look at the investment possibilities of various energy sources.

OIL AND GAS

About 2,000 years ago, one of the more important uses of crude oil in the Middle East was in the treatment of camel mange. Since that time the use of petroleum has increased substantially as well as diversified. More than $60 billion is now invested in the oil and natural gas industry in the United States. It is the largest single business in the world. Abroad, investment is huge and spiraling upward rapidly. At the present time, oil and gas supply about three-fourths of the energy needs of the United States.

OIL

How would you like to find a million barrel oil field? Great! But how long do you think this million barrels would last the United States? I have asked people this question during the process of lecturing on the general topic of oil, and have gotten answers which range upward to a month. What is your guess? The answer: *Less than 3 hours!*

We now use about 11 million barrels of oil a day in the United States. In another 10 years we will use at least 14 million barrels a day. Oil use is going up even faster abroad. The search for oil is a tremendous race against consumption, and it is very big business. If you have to find a million barrels of oil every 3 hours or less just to stay even, it is a big venture!

Occasionally someone asks if atomic energy will replace oil. The answer is that the two don't compete in many things (see chapter on THE ATOM). You cannot make plastics, insect sprays, or synthetic rubber out of uranium. As for competing in the energy field, the demand for energy is so great that all forms of energy must be drawn upon to help meet our needs.

Oil from wells will never go out of style until supplies are completely exhausted. You and I will not see that day. Long before that time, synthetic oil from oil shale or from the hydrogenation of coal will have begun to take over to replace oil from wells.

Ways of investing in oil.

You can invest in oil in several ways. Here are some:

1. You can form your own oil company and go out and look. (That's what Harry Sinclair did.)
2. You can go into partnership with other investors and drill certain leases offered you, or which you locate yourself.
3. You can buy shares in relatively small private ventures which either drill wells or buy production, or both.
4. You can buy leases on lands which are potentially oil-bearing and try to sell these leases later to oil companies for them to drill, retaining for yourself a small percentage of the royalties (called "override").
5. You can invest in stocks of publicly held companies, such as Texaco, Standard of California (sometimes called Socal in broker's terminology), Standard Oil Company (N. J.) (commonly known for convenience in conversation as "Jersey" or "Jersey Standard"), Gulf, and others.

Forming your own company, or a few people getting together and going out to look for oil, was the way many companies got started. That era has largely, although not entirely, passed. The easy oil has been found, and this approach is not feasible for most of us any more.

Selling participation units (an eighth, 1/16th, 1/32nd, et cetera) in drilling ventures to small investors has been popular at times (this was done by mail in the 1950's to a considerable extent—the sad case of Admiral Oil in Oklahoma is an example). Most of these drilling ventures were marginal, the "office overhead" (another name sometimes for fancy salaries and expenses for the promoters) was high, and the results on the average not very good. I checked into several rather closely, and found the outcome ranged from poor to thoroughly dismal. A few have been successful. If you are going to participate in private drilling ventures, it might be well to get some professional advice. By this I mean ask a reputable petroleum geologist—a member of the American Association of Petroleum Geologists which has a code of ethics it enforces (you can get names of members near you—they are in every state virtually—by writing this organization at Box 979, Tulsa 1, Oklahoma), or a member of the American Institute of Professional Geologists (P. O. Box 836, Golden, Colorado). If the geologist is not a member of one of these organizations I would have some doubts about his qualifications to render a worthwhile opinion. Usually you must invest several thousand dollars, at least, to buy into private drilling ventures. Good advice will cost only a small fraction of your investment. I am constantly amazed at people who will put their money into the wildest sorts of oil or mining schemes with little information or any competent advice. It is no different from going to the local butcher shop to have your appendix removed. The chances for survival are slim.

The drilling of oil wells through participation in small or private drilling ventures has some advantages and some disadvantages. The advantages are chiefly tax-wise but unless you are in a high tax bracket, the disadvantages may outweigh the advantages. The disadvantages relate chiefly to the fact that unless you drill a lot of wells you can't get on the right side of the law of averages unless you are lucky. Only one wildcat in 43 finds a million or more barrels of oil, and you might have to drill 50 or more wells before you get a discovery. I know of a major company that drilled over 100 wildcats before hitting oil in one area. Where would they have been if they had stopped at number 99? If you just drill one or two wells you are not able to take advantage of the law of averages. You can be like the statistician who drowned in a stream with an average depth of 6 inches. A company drilling in a wildcat area like the Oregon continental shelf or along the Alaskan coast, must be able to write off the whole area (millions of dollars) if necessary, against discoveries in such good areas as Libya or Saudi Arabia.

Buying oil production.

For various reasons (financial problems of the operators who become temporarily over-extended, to settle estates, et cetera) it is sometimes possible to buy production on a profitable basis—that is, buy producing oil wells which have years of life left. This, as opposed to drilling exploration (wildcat) wells, may not have quite the tax appeal for high-income, high tax-bracket investors; but for the average investor it has other things to recommend it. First, this procedure is a relatively more certain way of investing profitably in oil, than buying into wildcat drilling ventures. The decline curve on an oil well after it has been producing for several months, is a reasonably predictable thing. Also, secondary recovery methods (water-flooding, for example) sometimes recover additional oil beyond that obtained from initial flowing and pumping of the well.

The chief pitfall I have observed in this approach to oil investment is that there is a tendency for the marginal wells and fields to be for sale. An unwary investor may find himself barely getting his money back about the time the wells stop producing (or they may stop before he gets his money back). It pays to study the situation carefully in advance of buying.

If you live in an oil-producing area, you can occasionally buy local production yourself; but then you have management problems which, with an oil well or field, can be considerable. From having owned interests in oil production in both Oklahoma and Texas, I can personally testify that managing production is not something you can easily handle part-time. To solve this problem for the small investor, a few investment firms from time to time have put together what are called "production packages" (assembling a group of wells and operating them under one set of books), provide management for them, and sell units in these production packages to investors. One firm which does this is Craig-Hallum, Inc., of Minneapolis. Chiefly through contacts with a Texas oil company, Atoka, Inc., Craig-Hallum makes it possible for upper Midwest and Eastern investors to put money into producing oil wells.

Package deals in drilling ventures.

To get the individual on the right side of the law of averages, some package exploration deals are set up whereby you participate with other individuals in a number of drilling ventures in a given year. Thus you don't have all your money riding on one well. This exploration "package" may cost 10 to 15 thousand dollars per unit, and you can buy as many units as you wish in several different projects. Several organizations offer this sort of arrangement (for example, Apache Corporation of Minneapolis; Prudential Drilling Funds of New York), and usually the managements of these companies invest some of their own company money in the project. Some of these have done well; they have the advantage over other private ventures in that they are somewhat larger, usually, and can employ one or several full-time geologists. Nevertheless, to beat the bigger companies which have greater resources in the form of exploration personnel, experience, and equipment (and oil exploration takes a lot of very technical equipment and personnel), you need an extraordinarily smart group of people. There are some. Check closely on the records of these companies offering "package" drilling deals, and, again, if you are putting a lot of money into them, it will usually pay you to get your own professional consultant to look after your interests.

Leases.

Forty acre public land leases were peddled by mail for a number of years until various methods were used to reduce this traffic. Most (I am tempted to say all) of these mail-order lease offers were close to frauds. The advertising stated there was "a chance" of finding oil and gas in these areas. What these chances were interested me sufficiently to check up on just exactly where some of these offerings were located. I found certain of the lease lands underlain by granite! Granite is a rock which was once molten, and most granite has no bottom for all practical drilling purposes. Furthermore, any oil in the area would have been destroyed by the invasion of the molten granite. Chances of finding oil in such a locality, in my very considered professional opinion, would be substantially less than a million to one, but I suppose there always is a "chance." (And that is what the ads said—they didn't quote the odds.)

Valid lease brokers do exist, however, and in oil producing states such as Montana, Wyoming, Oklahoma, and Texas, good leases are sometimes sold, but sold for good money and not by mail, 40 acres at a time, for $160. Trading in oil leases is a highly specialized art, and success is based on knowing the area in detail. It is no field for amateurs. If you consider becoming involved in this sort of thing, obtain expert advice. It will be cheap at any reasonable figure.

Investing in stocks of publicly held oil companies.

This is the sort of oil and gas investment most readily available to most of us, and usually the most satisfactory and problem-free and profitable in the long run. All major brokerage firms and even some larger banks (Chase-Manhattan, for example) have petroleum research sections, for oil investment is a tremendous outlet for capital. A large amount of information about oil companies is published by brokerage firms, and you can get this from their local offices or by writing to their research departments. In this regard, it is interesting to discover that opinions frequently differ widely on the relative investment merits of various oil company stocks. By using a few relatively simple yardsticks, however, even the small investor can get some idea of values of oil company stocks—at least in comparison with one another. In the next few paragraphs are some suggestions as to how to make these calculations. Ultimately your opinion may be just as good as that of a brokerage firm; possibly better. In the past, if that is any example, I have seen some rather obviously undervalued situations exist for prolonged periods of time. Pure Oil was a classic case in point. In following these undervalued situations, I found that sooner or later they either moved up sharply in price to more nearly their true value, or they were merged into other companies at a nice valuation.

Detecting undervalued oil stocks.

Undervalued situations in oil stocks develop rather frequently because the industry moves relatively rapidly, and these changes in positions of the various companies are not always promptly reflected in stock quotations. In the next few paragraphs I think it may be possible to give you enough basic information so you have the possibility of success in recognizing some undervalued situations yourself. I will cite Pure Oil again as a good example of what can be done. Pure Oil had a good lease position. That is, the land they had under lease had better than average promise as being eventually productive. This could be determined simply by noting how many acres the company had and in what areas. In 1958, for example, wildcat well success percentage (all wildcat wells drilled by all companies) was 12% in Colorado and 27% in Louisiana. For each foot of well drilled in Colorado that year, 3.2 barrels of oil were discovered; in Louisiana 21.1 barrels per foot were found. These are state averages, of course, and any single lease can be an exception; but if a company has lease positions in various areas of the state they are going to come somewhat close to the average results for that state. It should be pointed out, of course, that drilling was deeper in Louisiana than in Colorado, on the average, and therefore more costly per foot. But the greater amount of oil found per foot drilled in Louisiana more than compensated for the higher drilling cost—one reason why the major oil companies are moving heavily into the Gulf Coast, and have been pulling out of the Rocky Mountains, to some extent, in recent years.

You as a small investor might say that these figures on relative success percentage and barrels of oil found per foot drilled for various areas are not public information—that I got them because I am a geologist. Not so. These figures I found in an information leaflet on the table with other literature in a brokerage office (Harris, Upham and Company) one afternoon.

In any event, Pure Oil had extensive leases in coastal Louisiana, a good location. What its refineries and other equipment were worth was plainly stated in the annual report, and the oil and gas reserves were also listed. Later in this chapter, figures are given which you can use in calculating oil and gas values.

Adding up all the solidly-based figures (refinery value, value of oil and gas, et cetera) and tossing in their lease position at virtually nothing, Pure Oil looked like a very undervalued situation, worth a minimum of $60 a share, and perhaps more. It was selling then for around $34. I bought some, and for a long time the price would move up and down in the $30 to $45 range. When it moved down into the $30 range, I would buy, and when it moved up 8 or 10 dollars and hesitated there, I would sell. But one day in 1964 Pure Oil started to move up and it didn't stop in the $40 range—it kept right on up to nearly $70 a share because some other companies suddenly realized it was a bargain and they offered to buy the company. Control was

finally purchased by the Union Oil Company of California
at a price which some Pure Oil stockholders thought was
too low, and for awhile they threatened court action but
nothing came of this. These stockholders may have had a
point; my figures indicated that Union Oil certainly did not
pay more than they should have for Pure Oil.

At a price of $30 to $45 a share, where Pure remained
for a long time, the calculation that it was an undervalued
situation was one which almost anyone could have made. But
that is all over and Union has Pure. Next logical step is to
recalculate the value of Union Oil and see whether or not
its present market price takes into consideration all the
assets of Pure (as well as the good holdings of oil shale which
Union has—see figures on this in the chapter on OIL
SHALE). This sort of thing can be both a fascinating and a
profitable use of your time.

Some factors determining value of oil stocks.

Here are a few simple facts and figures which will help
you make your own calculations on the worth of a particular
oil stock. The exact value of a barrel of oil in the ground
may be subject to some argument; but if you use the same
figure for all oil companies (making the distinction, of
course, between a barrel of oil in the U. S. and one abroad),
you will at least get some relative comparison of value
whereby you can determine that one stock is a better buy
than another. The exact length of the stick you use for a
measure is not important so long as you use the same stick
to measure all companies.

First, it is important to recognize that there are several
kinds of oil companies:

1. *A crude producer.* This is a company which only finds and produces oil, but does not refine or market it. Examples are Superior Oil Company, and Amerada Petroleum Corporation.

2. *An integrated company.* This is a company which produces, refines, and markets oil. There are varying balances among these activities in different companies. If a company produces more crude oil than it refines, it is called a "crude producer on balance." (Example: Gulf Oil). If it refines or markets oil principally, it is called a "refiner on balance" or a "marketer on balance." Sinclair Oil does not produce all its own crude needs; many other companies are in this position,[1] which is not necessarily bad. From time to time the crude producers have done better than those who primarily refined and marketed oil. At other times the reverse has been true. As of 1965, over the previous 5 years, "crude rich" companies averaged about 20.6% operating profit margin, whereas "crude poor" companies had about an 18.4% return.

3. *A distributor and/or marketer.* These companies buy all their oil products and distribute them to independent oil stations (cut-rate brands, commonly), or market the oil through their own stations (local or regional brand names). There are

---

[1] As of 1965, Gulf produced 173% of its own refinery needs, Texaco 136%, Marathon 121%, Standard of California 119%, and Continental 112%. Companies producing less crude than their refinery needs included Atlantic 89%, Phillips 87%, Jersey 85%, Sun 85%, Union 74%, Mobil 71%, Shell 63%, Tidewater 58%, Cities Service 52%, Standard of Indiana 50%, Sinclair 44%, and Sohio 26%.

many such companies. This is not an oil company in the sense of our discussion, as it does not own natural resources itself but simply sells them.

The point is, when you buy stock in an oil company, you may be buying oil in the ground (crude reserves); you may be simply buying some refineries, or tank trucks, or filling stations; or you may be buying all of these things (which would be the case of a fully integrated company). Determine first of all what kind of an oil company the company is.

I should add that there is another kind of oil company coming on the scene—a company which is diversifying into other things besides oil to a greater or lesser extent (things beyond related industries such as petrochemicals). Sunset International Petroleum [2] is an example. Because of its well-located California land holdings, it now has become primarily a real estate developer, currently obtaining only 25% of its income from oil and gas. Reserve Oil and Gas Company bought out Apple Valley Building and Development Company, a concern developing a desert home community about 100 miles northeast of Los Angeles. Other companies also have been widening their interests. Signal Oil owns 48% of American President Lines (steamship company), and recently Signal bought Garrett Company, an aircraft parts and equipment manufacturer. Signal, however, remains very much an oil company with extensive oil and gas properties worldwide. Occidental Petroleum is involved in sulfur mining, fertilizers, chemicals, and the real estate and lumber businesses, besides oil and gas production.

―――――――

[2] Name changed 1966 to Sunasco, by merger.

Some basic figures.

There are 42 U. S. gallons in a barrel of oil (35 Imperial—Canadian or British—gallons). Oil in the ground proved up by drilling is called "proved reserve." In the United States, oil in the ground can conservatively be valued at from $1 to $1.50 a barrel. Currently gas is worth about 10 to 12 cents a thousand cubic feet (see chapter on NATURAL GAS). I am reasonably certain, from all figures I can obtain, that the cost of finding oil in the United States is now at least $1.50 a barrel; but in checking with the investment department of one large bank I found, as of 1965, they were using the figure of $1 a barrel for oil reserves, and 7 cents a thousand cubic feet for gas. Both figures are conservative in my opinion, and if you can find an oil company selling for this sort of valuation, you have found a bargain. To this, add the value of the refineries, petrochemical plants, et cetera (shown on balance sheets), and you have a basic value figure.

What I have just said applies chiefly to domestic oil companies, or at least oil and gas in the United States and Canada. As time goes by, more and more companies have holdings abroad—the center of the oil industry is shifting toward the Middle East. What is oil and gas worth in such areas? This is close to the $64 question—nearer the $64 million questions, and in a few cases much more, and here political uncertainties come into the picture. Right now gas reserves in the Middle East cannot be given a figure that is very realistic (see comments in the chapter on NATURAL GAS). Depending on politics, oil is no doubt worth more in one country than it is in another. I asked several large investment firms about this, and a couple of them ventured the average figure of around 50 cents a barrel. Again, perhaps the exact figure is less important than simply being sure to use the same figure for all companies so that a comparison can be made. The problem with this is that the figure probably should not be the same for every country—politics make the difference, and at this point you are on your own. (For a fascinating and humorous look at the inside of an oil camp in the Middle East, and to get some feel for international politics regarding oil, read *Big Oil Man From Arabia,* by M. S. Cheney, Ballatine Books, New York, 1958).

Again, as in the case of domestic companies, plus-factors in foreign operations would include a good lease position and a vigorous exploration program. It costs money to send a crew to Libya to explore. The fact that crews are out exploring means substantial money has been spent even if nothing has been found. From this effort there will be a lot of valuable information in the company files. This can't be given an exact dollar figure, but just add it in as a plus-factor over the company which does not have an active exploration program. Ordinarily, the annual report will tell about any major exploration programs, and something of their progress.

In any case, you can usually add up some rough figures on the companies, divide out the figures by the number of shares outstanding, and come up with some interesting comparisons. By this simple procedure I determined one time that Southern Production Company (operating in Canada) had a very large amount of oil in the ground considering the low price of the stock (then $26). I bought some immediately because the figures looked so good, and while I was recalculating things just to be sure. Sinclair, apparently, had been doing some figuring too, and decided it was cheaper to buy Southern Production Company than try to find that much oil, and offered $38 a share for the company. It was subsequently sold to Sinclair.

As companies explore, buy and sell leases, have better or poorer luck in drilling, devise new methods for recovering more oil from existing fields (many fields initially yield less than half of the oil there), the values behind the various oil company stock shares change. Frequently it takes time for the financial community to become fully aware of this. Buying opportunities develop, and with some fairly simple calculations you may have the basis for discovering some undervalued situations.

Getting information.

Most annual reports of oil companies are quite informative. A few are not, but on the other hand some companies put out supplements to their annual reports which give very detailed information for those who really want to study the situation. (Mobil Oil now does this.) Perhaps you may not have noticed, but more and more companies are widely advertising free copies of their annual report; so getting them, whether you are a stockholder or not, is easy. It just costs a postage stamp. Also, most brokerage firms put out a great variety of statistical information, and their research department can get you more if you wish. It is no problem to get enough facts to make some very enlightening comparisons among companies as to values. It is a fascinating occupation and one which will pay excellent returns if you give it reasonable effort and thought. Based on some 20 years of trading in oil stocks in strictly a small investor way, my results show a few losses but on balance the results have been very good, using no more information than what most anyone can easily acquire.

Adequately evaluating a big corporation such as Standard Oil Company (N. J.) is perhaps beyond the scope of the average investor; but numerous smaller and more simply organized companies exist for you to investigate. Also, there are several information services which offer comments and facts about oil stocks to investors for a small fee. One of these is John S. Herold, Inc., 25 Greenwich Avenue, Greenwich, Connecticut, which publishes the *Petroleum Outlook*. I have no connection with this firm but have used their service. They dig out an impressive array of figures and partially digest them for the average investor; and in doing this I think they have done the investment community a real service. Future performance may be different, of course, but to date they have proved to have good information. Such large brokerage firms as Merrill Lynch occasionally put out entire booklets on the oil industry and on certain oil companies. These are free for the asking and provide a fertile field for study. I should add that in the 20 years I have followed oil stocks, there has never been a time when there was not at least one oil stock of a reasonably well known company which was not undervalued (as proved by subsequent price rise), so any time, apparently, is a good time to make a study to try to find such situations. As a reader you may ask why I don't list such situations here. The reason is that if I did so, 5 minutes after the book came out the price of the stocks would move up, and the statements as to what stocks were undervalued would no longer be true. But there are at least 3 such situations right now in listed securities—at least they are good enough so that I am willing to put a few dollars in each of them. You can find these, and others, I am sure.

Politics and oil—an explosive mixture.

The topic heading just given is a variation of a talk title I once used for an address before the Minneapolis Kiwanis Club—"World Oil and World Politics." Minnesota being a state which does not produce oil, the whole matter seemed a little vague to my audience until I pointed out that the United States as a whole with 3½ million square miles of area has about 35 billion barrels of oil, whereas Kuwait with an area of 8,000 square miles has about 63 billion barrels of oil! *Nearly 80% of the world's oil reserves are in the Middle East and North Africa.* This is what all the international tug of war is about in that part of the world, and many American companies are involved.

Gulf Oil Corporation has the great fortune—or misfortune—of having exceedingly large oil reserves in Kuwait. Gulf found some tremendous oil fields but as a result it has most of its eggs in one basket. Gulf has tried to achieve a better geographic (or to put it plainly—political) distribution of its oil reserves. They bought out a majority interest in British American Oil Company (of Canada) with this objective partly in mind. But Gulf still has a large percentage of its oil reserves in Kuwait—and relatively speaking a lot of oil behind each share of stock. But is Gulf a bargain? Or is it fully priced, considering international uncertainties? Just as I write these lines, Syria has ordered nationalization of all oil companies. Make up your own mind. Geological factors and economics I can understand to a fair degree. Foreign politicians (not to mention domestic) I cannot. If you want to ride both horses at the same time, buy stock in an international oil company, and at the same time—as a hedge against the possibility that things might get rough in the Middle East—put some of your money into our tremendous oil shale deposits which are our chief and very potent protection against any oil shortage which might develop because of overseas complications. Actually, you can really just put your money in one of several companies which already themselves have hedged their positions by having not only overseas production in quantity, but have bought into oil shales in the U. S. (See chapter on OIL SHALE for list of companies with major holdings in oil shale.)

In my opinion, the chances are good that both avenues of investment will be favorable. The Arabs can't drink the oil—they have to sell it to buy refrigerators, and other comforts of life, not to mention the necessities. At the same time the demand for energy is going to increase so rapidly that our oil shales are even now coming into commercial production in a small way.

And for both foreign oil operations, and for the development of our domestic oil shales, a great deal of money will be needed, so your investment capital will find many outlets.

Summary.

There are several ways you can invest in oil. For most people, buying oil company stocks is the most logical and satisfactory approach. Careful comparative evaluations of companies will show some are definitely better buys than are others. Smaller companies lend themselves to analysis more readily than do larger companies, and the picture may change more quickly with a small company because one or two major discoveries are relatively more important percentage-wise to its total oil reserves than in the case of a huge company.[3] These smaller situations, therefore, offer the more promising places for investors to look. Also, smaller companies which are undervalued tend sooner or later to be bought out by larger companies, usually at prices substantially above the prevailing market price.

You can also participate in oil finding and development by buying into "package" drilling deals, but in such cases it is well to enlist some competent geological advice. Buying proven production (producing oil wells) is a possibility, also. This offers a relatively conservative, predictable way of entering rather directly and quickly into the oil industry.

The demand for energy is great. It is rapidly growing even larger. Oil stocks remain prime investments. Undervalued situations seem to exist at all stages of the general

---

[3] Lowry Investments, Inc., of Colorado Springs, Colorado, make this point very well in a leaflet they published titled "Speaking of Low Priced Stocks." They state, "The 'blue chip' $10 billion Standard Oil Company of New Jersey may drill into a new oil field worth $10 million. $10 million added to $10 billion would increase company value by only .1% (one tenth of one percent). But if a small $500,000 oil company discovered the same $10 million oil field, the increase in equity would be 20-fold—that's a 2,000% profit!" They also point out the matter of leverage in stocks of companies with small capitalization, stating, "A good illustration was Bonanza Oil Company who struck oil in Washakie County, Wyoming, in the early '50's. The Bonanza field has since produced over 30 million barrels of oil from about 540 acres—less than one section. The stock advanced from 50¢ to $20.00."

stock market. Any time is a good time to look for them and buy them.

It should also be added that some mutual funds tend to specialize in oil stocks to a greater or lesser extent, and at least one closed-end investment company, Petroleum Corporation of America (listed New York Stock Exchange), invests only in oil and gas shares, or in closely related enterprises. Like most closed-end funds, Petroleum Corporation commonly sells at a discount from its net asset value, which adds attraction to its situation.

NATURAL GAS

As long ago as 1000 B.C., the Chinese were drilling wells for natural gas, piping it some distance in bamboo pipelines for use in heating houses and for light. They had a good thing and we apparently think so too, for we now have in the United States over half a million miles of natural gas pipelines. More are being constructed every day (30,000 miles a year). Natural gas use in the United States will at least double during the next 20 years.

In 1965, Ira Cram, chairman of the executive committee of Continental Oil Company, predicted that by 1980 the U. S. would be consuming 26 trillion cubic feet of gas per year. Put another way, this would mean that from 1965 to 1980, the U. S. will consume 344 trillion cubic feet of gas, compared with 243 trillion cubic feet consumed from the beginning of the time natural gas was first used in the U. S., up to 1964.

Natural gas use is growing faster than any other fuel in the United States (except the atom, which started from a zero base not long ago). Unfortunately, it is not growing so fast in terms of how much natural gas we are finding to supply these huge demands. In 1946, we had about 32 times as much natural gas reserves proved up in the ground, as we used in one year. Now, although we have more than twice as much natural gas in reserves, our rate of consumption has gone up so that this represents only about a 19-year supply. With some natural resources the problem is demand— markets. For example, we have a superabundance of clay from which to make any and all the bricks we need. But in the case of natural gas, the demand is there and growing fast. Supply is the concern.

Nevertheless, answers to the supply problem will ultimately be found, but these answers will cost money—and in turn investors will have further outlets in which to profitably place their capital. Later in this chapter we will mention some of these possibilities, and the long range prospects, for natural gas.

Gas reserves.

For the next 20 years at least, the supply of natural gas in North America seems adequate to take care of the projected needs and expansion of this industry. Where are these gas reserves and who has them?

Geologists have argued for a long time, inconclusively as far as I can tell, as to whether or not they could go out and explore for gas, not oil. The fact is that most gas has been found by people who thought they were looking for oil. Almost all oil has some gas dissolved in it and when 100 barrels of oil are produced from a well, many thousand cubic feet of gas are usually produced. There are a few gas fields, however, with little or no oil (the great Hugoton Field on the Kansas-Oklahoma border, for example). Also, in recent years some very large individual gas wells have been found in Canada.

When you talk about gas reserves, you have to get used to big figures. Fortunately, hearing about the national debt has conditioned us to this sort of thinking, although natural gas gets you involved in even bigger figures, impossible though that might seem. Gas, in quantity, is figured in thousands of cubic feet, the unit being a thousand cubic feet and written Mcf. For example, 4,650,000 cubic feet of gas would be 4,650 Mcf.

Gas reserves in the United States are currently in the vicinity of 288 trillion cubic feet. How much natural gas there is presently proved up in the world, or even the Free World, nobody is really quite sure. For one thing, until recently, natural gas in the Middle East and North Africa was not a very important consideration. It was used locally, and most of the gas was simply pumped back down into the reservoir rocks to keep up pressure and keep oil flowing into the well bore.

Gas now shipped by tanker.

Gas used to be a continent by continent matter, because it could not be shipped by tanker as can oil. But recently all that changed. Ships have been built and are now operating which carry natural gas at a temperature of 260 degrees below zero (Fahrenheit). Natural gas can be shipped across oceans. This has been a major technological break-through. Three ships now carry gas from Algeria to Great Britain. More such ships are being built. An affiliate of the Standard Oil Company (N.J.) expects to invest $200 million the next few years in ships to carry gas from Libya to Italy and Spain. Jersey Standard has a 15-year contract to supply 110 million cubic feet of tanker-transported gas a day to Spain, and a 20-year contract to supply 235 million cubic feet a day to Italy, from fields in Libya.

How to invest in natural gas.

As gas and oil are found together for the most part, investing in oil companies with sizable gas reserves is the way to participate in this industry for most investors.

However, it is occasionally possible to buy gas wells and to market such supplies locally. Supplies of natural gas too small to be of interest to major companies, have sometimes been developed by an individual or by a local group of investors. But buying stock in oil companies with gas holdings is the easiest way to invest for most of us.

How much is natural gas worth when you add it into the value of an oil company, or calculated to the worth of a company which only produces and markets natural gas?

Location of gas makes difference in value.

How much natural gas is worth depends largely on where it is located relative to markets. Natural gas in the industrial eastern areas of the United States is more valuable than natural gas in west Texas. Gas prices at the well head might range from about 8 cents Mcf. to 18 cents or more. Giving it a value of about 10 cents Mcf. would be a reasonable average. By the time it gets to the consumer, of course, it costs a good deal more. These figures are for the United States. Gas in the Middle East and adjacent areas which now can be transported by tanker is another matter—a matter so new that I am not sure what such gas is worth. But it is apparent now that such gas, formerly ignored in calculating the worth of a company with foreign oil and gas reserves, must now be added into the value of a company. This is a good question to ask your broker's research department—the value of natural gas in foreign fields.

Value of gas per share—exercise in large figures.

Gas reserves are usually, though not always, stated in the company annual report. For exercise in large figures, try dividing the number of shares of stock into the number of cubic feet of natural gas reserves—which will give you so many cubic feet of gas per share. Figuring value of the gas at about 10 cents Mcf. calculate the worth of the company's gas reserves. Occasionally some "sleeper" turns up—a company which has, incidental to its oil drilling, been making gas discoveries which may not yet be fully tied into pipelines, and are therefore not contributing to company earnings for the time being. These things develop slowly, and then the increased inherent values seem suddenly to become apparent to followers of the stock market, and the price jumps up. Or, if it is a smaller company, another firm may decide to "find" gas by buying them out. With rising exploration costs, it is frequently cheaper in the United States especially, to obtain new oil or gas reserves simply by buying out another company which is undervalued, rather than going out and drilling for oil and gas.

One thing you will discover—it takes a lot of gas to add

up to significant value and earnings. However, some companies do have gas reserves large enough to be important on the balance sheet. Phillips Petroleum has some of the largest published gas reserves in the United States, currently about 18 trillion cubic feet. Humble Oil and Refining Company (a Jersey Standard subsidiary), does not publish its reserve figures, but it is my considered geological guess—although I want to frankly state it is just a guess—that they have the largest natural gas reserves of any single company in the United States.

There are gas companies—and gas companies.

Just as in the case of oil companies, there are several different kinds of gas companies. Some companies just produce gas (Hugoton Production Company), some produce and also market the gas (integrated companies such as El Paso Natural Gas), and some merely market the gas. In these cases, respectively, you are buying gas in the ground, or gas reserves plus pipelines and compressor stations and gas meters; or you may just be buying some pipelines and gas meters if you buy a company like Cascade Natural Gas Company which is only a marketer. El Paso Natural Gas Company, on the other hand, has substantial gas reserves, or contracts for reserves held by others, and has at its disposal at present a 26-year supply (based on current marketing needs) as compared with a general over-all industry average of about 19 years.

Summary.

The natural gas industry is growing fast—faster than the oil business. Being able to now transport gas by tanker across oceans gives this business further luster. Also, gas can be and is being produced from coal,[1] and it can also be obtained in great quantities, if necessary, from the oil shales of the Colorado Plateau. Buying interests in coal or in oil shale would be a long range way of investing in natural gas. But for the small investor it might be better to leave this sort of investing to the gas producers—just buy the stocks of these producers and let them find the reserves. Natural gas is a strongly growing industry with a bright future. Well selected stocks will be good investments.

TAR SANDS

Tar sands are sands soaked with tar or heavy oil (and there are all gradations between). In general, oil gets into these sands either by forming in, or migrating into them. Then the lighter fractions of oil evaporate leaving the heavy oil or tar behind.

Oil obtained from tar sands usually is of lower quality than much of the oil obtained from wells. But chemists can do wonders with it and produce some very satisfactory end products including liquid fuels similar to the gasoline obtained from ordinary crude oil.

[1] Strictly speaking, gas obtained from coal or oil shale is called manufactured gas, not natural gas.

Athabasca tar sands.

Some tremendous tar deposits exist. The largest is the Athabasca tar sand of northern Alberta, which is estimated to contain 625 billion barrels of oil. Not all of this is recoverable economically, but reliable figures indicate that recovery could run as high as 300 billion barrels—an amount enough to supply the United States at its current rate of oil consumption for more than 100 years. Putting it another way, 300 billion barrels of oil is more than the known reserves of the Middle East and South America put together.

These deposits have been known for years, and several times past, companies have tried to put them into commercial production. Until recently it seemed that the various processes tried were not efficient enough to make the price of this oil competitive with oil from wells. Now the picture is changing, partly because the price of oil from wells has been going up (exploration costs of locating wells go up, but this is not an item for tar sands—they have been found), and partly because a couple of companies apparently have worked out a process whereby the oil can now be economically recovered from these sands.

The Sun Oil Company owns 75% of Great Canadian Oil Sands, Ltd., which is spending $191 million building a plant that will be producing 45,000 barrels of oil a day, soon, from a lease which holds an estimated 650 million barrels of recoverable oil. Aside from the principal problem of how to physically separate the tar from the sand, the other two technological difficulties—working at outdoor temperatures as low as 50 degrees below zero, and disposing of all the waste sand without hauling it too far—have been solved.

The big advantage of the tar sands, in contrast to oil, as just stated, is that there is no cost involved in finding them. The tar sands are found. But until recently the sands have been just as good as lost. However, technology has now, in effect, "discovered" a new oil supply for us by releasing this great oil reserve on an economic basis. Returns from these deposits obviously can be large.[1]

Other tar and heavy oil deposits.

It should be added that various other natural tar or asphalt deposits are known in the western hemisphere. I once visited the great asphalt lake in Trinidad, where, after years of mining, the asphalt continues to ooze up out of the ground in seemingly endless supply. In Utah there is a solid black material called gilsonite which occurs in seams in sandstone. This has been worked for years (they mine the sandstone, crush it, and heat the gilsonite to get it out), and produces some oil. There are tremendous quantities of so-called "dead oil" (oil which will not flow into the well bore) in various parts of the United States, particularly Kentucky, Kansas, Missouri, Oklahoma, Texas, Wyoming, and California. Very large deposits of heavy oil exist in Venezuela. These deposits, called "Faja de Brea" (band of tar), which are not really tar but still fluid enough to be called oil, are estimated by Venezuelan officials to amount to more than 100 million barrels. If a method could be found to recover this oil economically, the company with this technical "know-how" could quickly

---

[1] Cities Service Company ("Citgo" of the filling station signs) also has substantial interests (30% in 300,000 acres) in these tar sands.

add millions of barrels to its oil reserves. Many methods are under study and various financial journals report on these efforts from time to time. This line of research is worth watching as the stakes are large, and good investment opportunities will surely turn up from time to time, as technological break-throughs occur.

Summary.

Tar sands are being put into production right now in Canada. Heavy oil deposits occur in quantity in many areas, and much research is directed towards finding efficient ways of recovering this oil. Advances in techniques will undoubtedly be developed and with these will come investment opportunities. Almost all major oil companies are concerned with these deposits, either owning holdings in them, or doing research on recovery methods, or both. These companies include Cities Service, Sinclair Oil, Mobil, Sun Oil, Humble Oil and Refining Company (owned by Jersey Standard), and Richfield (recently purchased by Atlantic Refining Company).

OIL SHALE

Spiraling demands for energy, and especially for that versatile and easily transported energy source, oil, make certain that oil shales will be an important source of oil in the fairly near future. Shale oil already has a long and distinguished history which surprises many people. There were 30 crudely constructed shale oil plants in America supplying oil for lighting before 1776. The first big commercial plant to process shale oil was built in France in 1835, and another was soon built in Scotland. During the Second World War, Japan fueled its fleet in large part with shale oil, and the biggest shale oil plant today is in Communist China. All the gas used in the City of Leningrad in Russia is currently made from shale oil. Sweden, Estonia, and Spain have, or have had, shale oil plants.

But in the United States no really significant production of oil from shale has been accomplished to date. Oil from wells has been too convenient. However, *the United States has by far the largest oil shale reserves of any nation in the world: More than a trillion barrels!*

Oil shale occurs in at least 29 states and in Canada. The largest deposits are in ancient lake beds of Colorado, Wyoming, and Utah. Who first found these oil shales is unknown, but the story is told of an early pioneer who built a cabin and made a fireplace out of the very convenient naturally slab-shaped pieces of oil shale. He started a roaring fire in the fireplace and was considerably shaken to see the whole fireplace go up in flames! In this region, called the Colorado Plateau, there is estimated to be about 1.5 trillion (not billion but trillion) barrels of oil which can be recovered from oil shale. Some estimates go as high as 2 trillion barrels. This is equal to about 50 times the present proved oil reserves of the United States. *These oil shales constitute the most valuable single mineral deposit we have.*

Oil shale—no oil and not shale.

The term "oil shale" is slightly misleading in two ways —oil shale does not contain oil as such, and it commonly is not shale. It contains a variety of organic compounds collectively called kerogen. When heated, kerogen can be broken down into several liquids and gases that in turn can be rebuilt or altered by chemists to make products similar to, or identical with, regular petroleum products. Most of the oil "shale" is actually an earthy limestone or dolomite, but this is a minor technical point. Oil derived from shale is called "shale oil," so we have "oil shale" from which we get "shale oil."

Oil shale development—how soon?

No one really knows the answer to the question just posed, but everyone believes it is coming fast. Perhaps it is here now, for several companies have plans to build permanent plants soon, with no intention of discontinuing operations as has been the case in the past. Pilot plants are now operating. If commercial shale oil development isn't here now, it will be very shortly. The important fact is that the quantity of this resource is so great that it cannot be ignored. Also, here is a good example of how taxes and politics are perhaps the controlling factors rather than the matter of an adequate supply.

I am told that right now oil can be produced from shale at a price competitive with oil from wells, if all taxes were removed from it, and the $27\frac{1}{2}\%$ depletion allowance was applied to oil from shale as is now applied to oil from wells. Also, with the United States an ever-increasing importer of oil, foreign politics enter into the oil shale picture. Our foreign oil costs could go up suddenly, and our oil shale deposits could be commercial overnight even under present tax circumstances. This evening's headline from the Middle East may launch the United States' oil shale business tomorrow morning. This is one reason why the U. S. Bureau of Mines and many oil companies have, for a number of years, been experimenting with and gathering data on oil shale problems.

The experiemental oil shale plant at Rifle, Colorado, has been opened and shut a couple of times, and is now operating again with several companies sharing costs of the work. A special agreement has been worked out whereby the results of this research will be made available to all companies much earlier than the usual length of time which patents run.

Oil shale problems.

One could write a book about oil shale—its potential and its problems—and such volumes have been written. The potential is obvious. Some of the problems include the fact that the area is located chiefly in the headwaters of the Colorado River, and water supply is a concern as Arizonans and Californians both use Colorado River water. Another problem is disposal of waste. Even in rich shales, for every 2,000 pounds of oil shale mined, far more than half this amount must go back again as waste. I visited Rifle one time and a friend working at the plant there told me that the chief problem as he saw it, was to find a convenient place big enough into which the waste from the shale processing plant could be dumped. Hauling back to the mine nearly as much material as was hauled out originally is expensive; and if this double haulage could be eliminated it would raise efficiency greatly. My friend told me that the ideal situation would be to have a huge oil shale deposit located near the edge of the Grand Canyon, and then build a plant between the two—bringing oil shale in via the front door, and throwing the waste out the back door into the canyon. Unfortunately, no such handy situation seems to exist on the scale needed in the Colorado Plateau area, so this problem of waste disposal remains severe.

Another difficulty is the fact that it now appears some of the richest deposits of oil shale are out in the central portions of the basin and so deeply buried that they will have to be mined by underground methods. How to conduct mining underground on the scale required for oil shale work is a tremendous engineering challenge—it will be the greatest underground mining operation in the history of the world. It is a challenge but at the same time if a company or companies can solve the problem economically, this circumstance will present more investment opportunities.

Technology can certainly have a field day with oil shales —solving the problems of mining, waste disposal, the chemistry of the shale oil, and many other matters. Oil content ranges from as much as 100 gallons per ton, on down, with the average being about 15 gallons. Of course, the larger quantities of shale are in the lower grades, and here is the opportunity for companies through technological advances to "find" oil, by discovering how to profitably produce these low grade deposits. A part of the story, however, is related to the matter of who has the oil shales at present. This information is presented in subsequent paragraphs, and deserves careful reading.

Who has the oil shale deposits?

The picture on oil shale reserves of the various companies is changing moderately at the present time, because of exploration work and trades and purchases. Published figures are hard to obtain, but an estimate by the *Rocky Mountain Oil Reporter,* October, 1963, provides statistics which are probably still indicative today of the relative positions of some of the companies concerned. (This list does not include all companies with oil shale holdings.)

COMPANY	SHALE-BEARING ACREAGE	RECOVERABLE OIL (MILLIONS OF BBLS.) *	
Cities Service Oil	7,100	1,480	
Continental Oil	3,600	270	
Dow Chemical	7,900	2,312	
Doyle, et al. (1)	3,400	761	
Energy Res. Tech. Land (4)	17,500	4,550	
Getty Oil	17,800	4,186	
Gabbs Exploration (4)	5,000	550	
General Petroleum (1)	11,500	2,000	
Gulf Oil	1,600	133	
Humble Oil	640	200	(2,000)
Kerogen Oil Co.	1,400	196	
Massive Group	2,400	118	
Marathon Oil Co.	480	168	(1,500)
Pan. Am. (Std. Indiana)	1,500	205	
Parachute Oil Shale (1)	4,900	830	
Pure Oil Co. (2)	1,000	20	
Savage Shale (4)	17,600	4,186	
Shell Oil (3)	8,000	1,468	(8,470)
Sinclair	5,600	1,300	(3,100)
Standard Oil (Calif.)	50,600	9,248	

Texaco Inc.	14,000	1,626
Texas Nat. Petroleum (2)	1,400	74
Union Oil Co.		
California (4)	40,100	8,856
U. S. Naval Reserve	31,700	5,000
Wasatch Development		
Co. (4)	8,100	1,960
Weber Oil Co.	11,500	2,000

* From the minable section yielding 25 gal. oil/ton shale. Recoverable reserves may be 35% less from mining, crushing, and retorting losses. Reserves may be much larger by *in situ* retorting of several sections.

( ) Figures in parenthesis are reserves calculated on basis of *in situ* production or open-pit mining of multiple sections. *In situ* production would be accomplished by such methods as burning the shale in place and not mining it.

1 Owned or controlled by Mobil.

2 Owned by Union Oil Co.

3 Owned or under option (refers to amount of acreage).

4 Includes unpatented mining claims (status of these somewhat in question, currently).

The great bulk of the oil shale deposits (79%), however, are still owned by the Federal Government, and the really big question is on what basis the Government will turn over these lands for development. The Secretary of the Interior has recently asked Congress to decide this question. To give you some idea of the importance of this decision, consider the fact that the Shell Oil Company proposed that it be granted leases on 50,000 acres of oil shale lands in the central part of the rich Piceance Basin in Colorado. This land is esti-mated to contain 150 billion barrels of oil which would suffice to cover all the Shell's oil requirements at the present rate of refining in this country for an estimated 660 years. It is equal to about 5 times the presently proved oil reserves (35 billion barrels) in the entire United States. Chronically oil-short Sinclair requested lands which would suffice that company at current requirements for about 226 years. In some parts of the Piceance Basin, the shale beneath an acre of ground contains 2½ million barrels of oil, or 1.6 billion barrels per square mile.

All this adds up to "The oil shale policy problem" which is the title of a special publication put out by the U. S. Department of the Interior in July, 1964, from which some of the foregoing statistics were taken. A summary statement in this publication is most significant: "Despite the somewhat vague picture of oil-shale economics . . . the position seems clear that an oil-shale industry is at least marginally competitive with the petroleum industry today."

Who will make the first move?

Several companies are on the verge of commercial shale oil production right now. The Oil Shale Corporation (traded over the counter) together with Standard Oil of Ohio and Cleveland-Cliffs Iron Company formed a venture group (Colony Development Company) to get into shale oil production. Shale oil production, at least in a small way, is virtually here now. It is probable that all the companies just listed, with substantial holdings in oil shale, will be entering the business within the next few years. The move into shale oil processing will take place slowly, but steadily. It should be noted also that the Institute of Gas Technology reports that shale reserves in Colorado alone could produce 6 quad-rillion cubic feet of gas which is about 21 times the proved United States gas reserves (288 trillion cubic feet). With demand for gas going up more rapidly than even the demand for oil, this use of oil shale may come soon, also.

United States for oil shale investment.

The United States is the place to invest in oil shale, as we have both the largest reserves and probably also the largest market, currently, for the products of these deposits. Investment capital will surely be needed. *The Oil and Gas Journal* has reported that a 50,000 barrel a day plant would cost about $85 million. However, this compares favorably with costs of developing the Athabasca tar sand. According to this same *Journal,* a 45,000 barrel a day plant in the tar sand would cost about $190 million; a 100,000 barrel plant would cost $260 million. In both cases, capital costs are high and investors' dollars will be needed.

In investing in oil company stocks today, it is well to see what their oil shale lands might be worth, using perhaps the nominal figure of 25 cents a barrel of oil in terms of what can be recovered. This is a figure suggested to me by one invest-ment firm. They admit it is just a guess as there is no way of knowing at the moment the value of the oil to a company, but 25 cents a barrel is probably a minimum figure. Or you can use the index of what lands are now selling for. Oil shale lands which Dow Chemical purchased several years ago for $265 an acre brought an offer of $1,760 an acre from a major oil company recently—an offer declined by Dow. Several other companies have had similar great increases in the value of their land holdings, which they continue to carry on their books at very nominal figures, thus constituting, to some extent, a hidden value.

Summary.

Oil shale is going to be developed soon, and probably on a steadily increasing scale. The amount of oil involved is enormous, and these shales constitute the Nation's single most valuable mineral deposit. Development of these resources will require large amounts of capital, but the potential returns are also very great. Domestic and international politics, taxes, and technology all affect the future of oil shale. Some companies already have large oil shale reserves, but the Federal Government still holds an estimated 79% of the total. Decision on how the public lands will be opened to development is now being considered by the Government. It is probable that the ultimate decision will allow more companies to come in and develop this resource, offering additional opportunities for investment.

Note: I am particularly indebted to *The Oil and Gas Journal* and Mr. Edwin McGhee, the drilling editor, and to the *Rocky Mountain Oil Reporter*, Mr. Henry W. Hough, editor, for some of the statistics on oil, gas, oil shale, and tar sands presented in the several chapters concerned with these resources.

COAL

Some people are still under the impression that the coal business is dying. Nothing could be further from the truth. Especially in the United States the coal business is doing very well. It will almost certainly be doing even better in years to come. Here are some reasons why.

The coal mining business has changed.

There are several reasons why the coal mining business is improving. John L. Lewis has been one of them. He took his miners out on strike time after time, and forced the mine operators to mechanize. Now the amount of coal produced per man is very much greater than it was 30 years ago. A second factor is simply that demand for energy of all kinds is going up rapidly in the United States, as well as in the rest of the world, and coal is a good source of energy.

The principal use for coal is by utilities for the generation of electricity, and here two very significant developments are taking place to make coal competitive. One is the "continuous train"—trains which run night and day on a special track from mine to utility. This makes for more efficiency as much of the operation is automated. An improvement on the "continuous train"—actually eliminating the train—is the so-called "minemouth" generating plant, where the utility builds its plant at the mine, and coal is fed directly into the generating plant from the mine. This situation has the further advantage of not contributing to air pollution in city areas—a problem in the past with coal-burning utilities.

U.S. coal reserves—world's largest.

Here again, as with many other raw materials, the United States investor finds himself in a country with the world's largest supply of a vital material in which he can place his savings. Coal is now the top supplier of industrial energy in the United States. Coal's future is also favored by the fact that (with the possible exception of atomic energy) it represents the greatest energy reserve we have in the United States. There are about 10,000 tons of coal for every man, woman, and child in this country. *The United States has the largest coal reserves of any nation in the world.* We currently produce about 460 million tons a year; some experts predict we will be producing twice much 20 years ahead.

Coal's very formidable position in the United States energy reserve picture is clearly indicated by the following statistics (U. S. Bureau of Mines, 1960):

	RESERVES IN QUADRILLION B. T. U.	
KIND OF FUEL	PROVED	TOTAL POTENTIAL
Coal	5,400	22,000
Petroleum	215	2,355
Natural gas	285	1,100
Oil from oil shale	290	3,000

The potential for coal's future is large. With energy demands growing as they are, coal will surely be used in increased amounts, and the United States has the deposits. On the other hand, it is quite certain that much of our best coal (especially coking coal) has already been mined out; our reserves are largest in the lower grades. The coal mining industry will have to become highly technical, research and efficiency-minded, if it is going to do its part in our expanding energy-hungry economy. But the coal industry is becoming that way.

Coal looking forward to steady growth.

The coal companies lost markets heavily to the oil companies during the times when strikes were an annual event. The oil companies had, in John L. Lewis, one of the best friends they ever had—and I heard some oil company officials say just that. But the shift to oil, due to these strikes, is over, and from now on it is reasonable to expect that the coal business can look forward to a steady, solid growth. Coal, like oil, is not entirely at the mercy of nuclear power as a competitor, for coal is also a tremendous source of a great variety of chemical compounds which, of course, uranium can never be. Drugs, dyes, plastics, and literally thousands of other things are produced from coal; it is an exceedingly useful material.

Oil companies now interested in coal.

How is this for a switch? The oil companies, once fierce competitors of the coal companies, are now buying up coal companies. Here are a few examples of the trend. Continental Oil Company (Conoco) recently bought Consolidation Coal

Company [1] to form what company officials happily refer to as "this total-energy complex." With U. S. oil production beginning to top out, the fact that the nation's coal reserves represent the biggest single fossil fuel reserve we have is making the oil companies take notice—energy in the form of coal is estimated to be substantially more than 1,000 times the total energy consumption in the United States in 1960.

When you figure the value of an oil company (see section on evaluation of an oil company), search the balance sheet carefully for coal reserves. Why? Here is what one coal company executive recently said: "There is quite a bit of unpublicized oil company buying of coal lands. A lot of coal producers have been receiving merger feelers from the oil industry, including ourselves. Continental's purchase of Consolidation Coal is just the beginning of oil-coal mergers."

Some of this buying is already a public matter. Gulf Oil Corporation in 1963 acquired Pittsburgh and Midway Coal Mining Company which in 1964 was the 10th largest coal mining operation in the United States. Kerr-McGee Oil Industries, Inc. has obtained leases and prospecting permits on a total of 44,000 acres of coal land in the West; coal reserves in these lands are estimated at more than 660 million tons. A Kerr-McGee spokesman says, "Coal now is playing a revitalized role as an energy source in the U. S."

---

[1] Consolidation Coal Company is the nation's largest coal company in terms of assets and coal reserves (estimated at more than 5 billion tons), and as of 1964 its production of 45.4 million tons of coal was second only to the 46.6 million tons of coal produced by Peabody Coal Company.

Converting coal to oil and gasoline.

One of the principal reasons for oil company interest in coal is that coal can apparently now be made into a liquid fuel (even refined as far as gasoline, in effect), at prices very closely competitive with those of oil and gasoline obtained from wells. Jersey Standard began experimenting with this as far back as 1927. Several years ago, Mr. R. T. Haslam, then vice-president of the Standard Oil Company (N. J.) said in a speech entitled "World Energy and World Peace" given at the Massachusetts Institute of Technology:

> "For those energy uses that require liquid fuels such as in automobiles, buses, trucks, tractors, airplanes, we can convert coal to gasoline and oil through processes which have already been developed. The operating cost of these processes is not unreasonable, especially when we consider the unique advantages of liquid fuels and liquid fuel engines. Gasoline of exceptionally high grade can be made today from coal at about six cents per gallon above present costs of gasoline from crude oil.
>
> "It should be pointed out, however, that capital requirements for such energy conversion are tremendous. To produce only our present requirements of gasoline from coal would call for an expenditure of at least 20 billion dollars and would require 11 million tons of critical steel. Therefore, the development of synthetic fuels from coal should take place gradually and slowly over a long period of time as justified by economic conditions.
>
> "Therefore, we can say that there is sufficient

energy here in the United States in the form of coal—
which we know how to convert to liquid fuels—to take
care of all requirements for centuries to come. In a
world of peace without economic barriers our problems
are not severe."

More recently a U. S. Government estimate is that 100-
octane gasoline can be made from coal at a cost of 11 cents
a gallon, a price definitely competitive with present gasoline
at certain inland locations. A coal company executive, whose
company has been doing research on this matter says, "It isn't
a question of whether we can make gasoline from coal, it's
a question of which method and when."

Coal will heat homes again.

I can recall when the coal man came to our house every
month or two during the winter in Minnesota, and I shov-
elled coal into the furnace. Coal furnaces have lost popularity
in many parts of the country, and it was a great day for us
when we installed an oil burner. But coal will be coming
back again as a way of heating homes, to some extent.
Although nuclear power is becoming a major competitor of
coal in supplying energy for utility companies, coal will continue to supply an appreciable amount of this energy for a
long time and in this way coal will heat houses, as more and
more houses are electrically heated. My home is electrically
heated as are the homes of most of my neighbors here in
western Oregon. More recently, in my trips to the Midwest
and East I have noted that houses there are being built with
electric heat, something virtually unheard of there 10 years
ago. One estimate states that whereas we have only about a

million homes now being heated electrically, in 20 years we will have more than 15 million homes thus heated. In this way, by converting coal into electric power, coal will again be heating homes. "Coal by wire" is the phrase being used to describe this trend.

Possible value of mined-out coal company lands.

Coal companies frequently own in fee the lands they mine. And it has been notorious what some companies have done to this land—the utter chaos which resulted from strip mining operations. Caught by the squeeze of rising competition with oil, and low productivity per man, the coal companies had little choice but to strip the lands of coal as cheaply as possible and leave. Now, with machines contributing to much higher production per man, and with profit margins improved, the coal companies are taking strong action in the matter of reclaiming their mined-out lands. The Kentucky Reclamation Association, organized in 1948, now consists of 88 strip coal mining companies and 4 clay mining companies. They conduct research and experiments on converting the lands to wildlife habitats and recreational uses, among other things. Since 1948 they have planted more than 17 million trees.

Peabody Coal Company, the nation's largest coal producer, has a project called "Operation Green Earth." Through it they develop lakes, stock them with fish, and reforest the strip-mined lands. What potential these lands might hold for coal companies as sources of future income is still problematical. I wrote Peabody Coal Company on this matter, and Mr. Fred Buckner of their Public Relations Department very frankly replied to all my questions, and generously offered to let me quote any of this information, which I do here, in part:

"We have many thousands of acres of comparatively new stripping which have been planted to hardwoods and evergreens. It is too early in many cases to evaluate the economic returns on these lands through the harvest of timber and/or the sale of the lands, or the sale of the timber from those lands for pulp. This is a potential being researched, and the opinion of many experts is that substantial economic return to companies such as Peabody will take place over the next twenty to fifty years from this source.

"Where the nature of the spoil from the coal seam to the original surface is of the proper quality, we extensively grade these areas so that they may be traversed by cattle and by farm machinery. We have many thousands of acres leased to farmers for grazing purposes, and, in some cases, for the growing of crops. In the case of Peabody, this type of land use is mostly confined to our stripping operations in certain sections of Illinois and Missouri. Most of the lands we strip are sub-marginal as crop lands before stripping. Due to the rock and shale turned up in the stripping processs, most of these acres do not lend themselves to extensive grading and future use as grazing lands.

"In these areas, large bodies of water are created and, with the planting of forests on the spoil, represent the greater portion of our strip-mined areas. The best potential use for such areas seems to be development for recreational purposes, homesites, and for the cutting of timber as mentioned above.

"Not many strip mining companies actively operate

recreational areas themselves. Neither do they in general develop areas under their own corporation or subsidiary for real estate development. The usual practice is to sell these lands to private investors.

"To try to answer your question more directly, I think it is fair to say that most of the acres stripped do not at present produce income on a current or regular basis. However, with the population explosion in our country and the ever-increasing demand for outdoor recreation, there is no question but what these lands will be a tremendous asset to the coal companies and to the nation as they are developed to an even greater degree than has been done in the past.

"We have not attempted to give you any actual cost or profit figures since much of our conservation work has never been separated from our cost of operation. We are in the process now of changing our accounting system to separate these costs."

These comments may serve to give you a much broader view of coal companies' operations than what you had before. In any event, these lands are apparently at least minor sources of income now, and future income potential may be considerably greater. The fact that Peabody Coal is setting up a separate accounting system for this phase of operations indicates its growing importance.

Coal as an investment.

Whereas I do not think the coal business in general offers a spectacular growth rate, special situations such as mergers, new companies forming with new ideas on how to mine previously unprofitable coal seams, and new methods of coal mining used by operating coal companies, all offer speculative appeal to the coal industry, and underneath it all is a solid demand for more and more coal. Coal continues to be looked at with some skepticism by many investors because of its poor showing during the years that coal was going through its well-publicized troubles. Accordingly, many coal companies have presented excellent values in recent years. Some still do, and will continue to do so until the general public appreciates the fact that today's coal industry is far different from that of 20 or 30 years ago.

Mergers for more efficiency—special investment opportunities.

Coal companies with substantial reserves, emphasizing research on increasing their mining efficiency, are bound to have a good future. At the same time, smaller companies with good reserves may not have the money to spend on research, or to buy the giant shovels and other equipment needed to remain competitive. These may find it more attractive simply to sell out to larger companies—just as many small oil companies have done in the past. Here some interesting merger situations have already occurred, and more will probably appear.

Usually it is more profitable to buy into the company which is being merged rather than into the company which is taking over. The company being merged may have good coal reserves but may not be able to realize profits from them due to lack of equipment. Accordingly, the stock may sell at a substantial discount from what the company would be worth if it were part of a larger organization. Ordinarily the company making the purchase will buy the stock of the other company in the open market for a time; but this will gradually drive up the price of the stock, and sooner or later the word gets around that this is going on. Then the company will usually make a formal offer for the remainder of the stock. This bid will generally still be above the then market price of the stock. These situations are worth watching for, and have been quite profitable in the past. Now, with oil companies seeking mergers with coal companies, the investor has further reason for buying potential merger candidates. Money will undoubtedly be made from these circumstances.

Westward shift of coal activity.

Another factor for the investor to consider is that it seems likely that emphasis on coal mining in the United States will shift westward in the coming years—in fact, it is already doing so. Our largest reserves, although relatively low grade, are in the Great Plains and Rocky Mountains. Some of this land is Government-owned, but large areas are in private hands. About all that can be said of these circumstances, as they affect the individual, is that if he wishes to invest in the coal business directly (instead of buying stock in a large company), better opportunities will probably lie in these Western states. Western electric utility companies are using more and more coal.

If you are going to buy coal reserves, get good advice. In this connection it should be noted that various Government agencies, particularly the U. S. Geological Survey, and the U. S. Bureau of Mines, have been taking inventory of our coal reserves, and making maps of coal-bearing areas, for many years. Also, most state geological surveys have good information. If you want to invest in coal directly, contacting these agencies for basic information will be a great help to you.

Final investment comments.

There are many sound reasons for believing that coal mining is in a solid, long-term growth trend. The chairman of the board of Peabody Coal Company, Mr. F. S. Elfred, told the New York Society of Security Analysts recently that his company expected a growth rate of 7% a year for the next several years, at least.

There are many coal companies. Any good brokerage firm can give you a list of companies as well as make specific recommendations, if you want to invest in stock. It might be well to also point out that substantial coal deposits are held by companies which do not have "coal" in their names, and these, in effect, may have coal as "hidden assets"—at least they are hidden to the extent that much of the public is unaware of these coal holdings. Two of these are Utah Construction Company, and the Atchison, Topeka, and Santa Fe Railroad. There are others.

Coal, being both a good energy source and a versatile raw material, will be needed in ever-larger quantities. This is a vital business with a good future. Mechanization is now beginning to pay off. Remember again that the United States has the world's largest coal deposits. Canada also has substantial reserves.

ELECTRICITY

You can buy a ton of iron ore, or you can buy a ton of salt, just as these things exist in the raw state; but you can't buy a ton of electricity. You can only buy an interest in equipment which produces electricity. Ben Franklin's equipment was a kite and string. We use more complicated machinery now. Electricity is a natural resource which cannot be bought in the raw state by the ton or kite-stringful. However, electricity can be produced in many ways, as anyone knows who has scuffed his feet on a wool rug in dry weather and then touched some metal object (or some unsuspecting person's ear). But only one way is presently economical on a large scale and that is by means of generators—machines wherein a coil of wire is rotated in a magnetic field. But startling developments could come; for example, a material called cadmium sulfide [1] has the ability of converting light energy directly into electrical energy. Other materials can do this too, and a great deal of research is going into this problem of the direct production of electricity from raw materials (see chapter on FUEL CELLS). This is a field worth watching, for the investor. In the meantime, electricity is produced economically on a large scale only by generators powered by turbines which are driven by water, or steam (which in turn is formed by heat from the atom, coal, oil, or gas).

---

[1] In combination with other materials, through a process beyond the scope of this discussion.

Our most versatile energy.

There is hardly a more versatile and convenient form of energy than electricity. It can be transported instantly (or at the rate of 186,300 miles per second which is "instantly" for all practical purposes) over hundreds of miles, if necessary. It can be wired into remote places and made to do a fantastic number of diverse things from shaving you to letting you talk to somebody in Australia. You can even carry a certain amount of it around in a container called a battery.

Chiefly, predictions about the future of electricity all add up to two things: its use will continue to increase in the United States and Canada (and most other areas of the world) faster than the growth of the Gross National Product; in the United States since World War II, it has expanded 2½ times as fast as the GNP. And there is no foreseeable limit to its continued growth.

Investing in electricity.

Investing in electricity involves investing in equipment to make electricity, as we have stated. It also might involve investing in energy sources to power the generators, and these sources are chiefly coal, oil, natural gas, and the atom. Each of these energy sources will be considered separately in this book, as each has, except for the atom, a wide variety of other uses besides the generation of electricity. Suffice it to say that investing in electricity involves a number of fringe areas. For this discussion, however, let us stay with electricity as such, which means electric power plants.

We have gone through a time in the United States when public and private power companies have been vigorously jockeying for position. Now there seems to be some sort of established balance. Although the argument continues in local areas, the situation in general seems reasonably stabilized. Many private power companies do exist, and their growth rates can easily be determined—any brokerage firm has the statistics for you. The chief question is usually what you will give in the way of a high purchase price for a growth situation. Utilities in Texas, Florida, and Arizona, for example, have had and can be expected to continue to have high growth rates. Utilities in the Midwest and East have had lower growth rates, and are priced accordingly, *but all are growing*. It is hard to visualize an investment which has a more assured future and a steadier growth than a utility. Electric power company stocks should be in any reasonably diversified investment portfolio.

Consider electric equipment manufacturers, too.

Electrical equipment manufacturers should also be considered as a way, in effect, of investing in electricity. Technological break-throughs in production of electricity by direct means (from sunlight perhaps) on a commercial scale, could catapult some electrical equipment manufacturers into very profitable positions. This event is dependent on a great deal of research so, in my opinion it is the larger companies which are the more likely to make such discoveries if they occur.

Great demand for your investment capital.

Your money is going to be needed for investment in electric power. A recent ad sponsored by more than 300 investor-owned electric light and power companies includes this statement:

> "Within the next 10 years we'll approximately double the supply of electricity that we now have on tap. We'll build about as much as all we have built in the past 82 years. And in doing so, we'll put the savings of millions of investors to work in a way that benefits everyone."

Our private utilities will expand as much the next 10 years as their growth over the past 82 years—what a prediction! For more predictions on how electric power generation will grow and how the atom in particular will be involved, read the following chapter on THE ATOM.

THE ATOM

You will probably never use an atom-powered outboard motor. Gasoline is a most convenient source of energy for such mobile machines. But projected trends clearly indicate that the atom will be taking an increasing share of the job of producing energy—in the form of electricity. Coal, gas, oil, and water-power will be taking a lesser share percentage-wise as time goes by. (Demands on all forms of energy will increase in absolute amounts, however.) The Federal Power Commission and the Atomic Energy Commission have come up with the following predictions:

PERCENT OF ELECTRIC ENERGY GENERATED FROM VARIOUS SOURCES

SOURCE	Now	ESTIMATED IN 1980
Coal	54%	47%
Natural gas	21%	17%
Water power	19%	13%
Oil	6%	4%
Nuclear power	0.1%	19%

Atomic power already here.

Many people reading this book will be doing so by the light from electricity generated by the atom. Right now there are at least 13 civilian nuclear power plants producing about 1 million kilowatts. By 1968, a total of 21 plants are expected to be in operation producing more than 4 million kilowatts. Electric power spokesmen say that *after 1970 most of the new electric power plants will probably be nuclear.* Fuel-short areas, such as the northern Midwest, New England, Florida, and California, are likely to see the earliest and fastest development of atomic-powered electric generating plants. Already, there are six nuclear power plants built or planned for New England, including a $100 million project in Maine sponsored by eight utilities headed by Central

Maine Power Company. Certain isolated areas are logical sites for small nuclear power plants. The world's first atomic lighthouse, Baltimore Light, has been installed and is powered by a Martin nuclear generator—a product of Martin Marietta Corporation.

Demands on all energy sources will rise, approximately as indicated by the following figures (reference again to the Federal Power Commission, and Atomic Energy Commission):

	KILLOWATT-HOURS IN BILLIONS	
ENERGY SOURCE	Now	ESTIMATED 1980
Coal	494	1,264
Natural gas	201	458
Water power	166	340
Oil	50	107
Nuclear power	3	514

So, while coal is decreasing its percentage share of the market from 54 to 47, the total amount of energy which coal will supply will go up almost 300%, and the amount of coal used will rise by about this amount which is certainly faster than the rise in population in the United States. But atom-developed power will increase more than 150 times in this period. Bet on the atom!

How to invest in the atom.

How do you invest in the atom? Uranium and thorium have limited uses as raw materials as compared with oil or coal. Also, there is one mine in Canada which is reported to have more uranium than all the mines in the United States put together. But uranium is already in long supply, so buying into a uranium mine is not the immediate road to riches which many people once thought it was. As part of other, and larger income-producing operations, we do have several companies producing uranium in the United States. These include Atlas Corporation, Homestake Mining Company, and Kerr-McGee Oil Industries, Incorporated.

If you wish to invest in the atom, one of the better ways to do it might possibly be by putting your money into some application of the atom. By far the most obvious and promising one, as just described, is the atom for electric power generation. Utilities making use of atomic power are my top nomination for profitable and immediate investment in the atom.

One great application of electric power in the future (much more than it is being used today) is in the matter of space heating—heating homes and office buildings and factories. Natural gas and oil do a lot of this now, but as we become more and more an oil importer, the cost of gas and oil will go up. Furthermore, an eminent chemist has said he thought eventually there would be a law against burning oil in oil burners for simply heating homes—that oil is too valuable a combination of hydrocarbons to use this way. I think he is right. From oil and natural gas we can make thousands of things we can't make from uranium, such as plastics, fertilizers, insecticides, and synthetic rubber, just to name a few. Oil will eventually have to be saved for higher purposes than burning. As that time gradually comes upon us, we will fortunately have the atom working in a huge nationwide-tied electric power system.

The market for nuclear power equipment.

It is conservatively estimated that the market for nuclear power equipment the next 15 years in the United States is at least $10 billion, and nuclear installations in the rest of the world will involve from $10 to $27 billion. United States manufacturers of reactors, heat exchangers, and other nuclear plant equipment will undoubtedly get a substantial part of this business. Companies involved in development and production of nuclear power include General Electric, Babcock and Wilcox, Westinghouse, Allis-Chalmers, United Nuclear Corporation, Martin Marietta, and Combustion Engineering, Incorporated, among others.

Summary.

The uranium mining business offers a rather limited area for investment at the present time, although some companies do exist which get an appreciable part of their income from this source. However, the use of the atom in the generation of electric power is a field which is growing exceedingly rapidly. Bet on the atom—the electric way!

HEAT FROM THE EARTH

"Geothermal Heat: the Earth as a Power-Station," is the title of an article in a recent science journal. The temperature of the Earth increases, in its crustal portions at least, at the rate of about 1 degree Fahrenheit for every 60 feet of depth. Go down 6,000 feet and the temperature is 100 degrees hotter than the mean annual temperature at the surface. On this basis, the amount of heat energy (called "geothermal heat") in the Earth is staggering. This is not a new thought. In fact, we have been getting heat energy from the Earth commercially for many years.

Present geothermal plants operating.

In Italy, enough electric power is produced from steam generating plants deriving steam from wells, to run the entire Italian railroad system. Steam was first harnessed for use at the Larderello steam field (near Florence) in 1905. At present, by means of 160 steam wells, more than 350,000 kilowatt-hours are being produced there. New Zealand produces about 200,000 kilowatts, Iceland 17,000, Mexico 3,500, Katanga 275, Japan 60, and California (from an area about 75 miles north of San Francisco in Sonoma County) about 30,000 kilowatts. More steam wells are being developed in California and elsewhere.

I was interested to learn, while working as a consulting geologist for an oil company exploring in Nevada in 1964, that many of the geyser and hot spring areas of that state have been leased, principally by one company. This company, in partnership with an oil company (which presumably has the drilling "know-how") plans to systematically develop these Earth-heat sites. Chief attraction is the fact that reserves of Earth-heat are apparently unlimited for all practical purposes, as compared with oil reserves, for example, which are being depleted by each producing well. There are problems, however, the principal one being that rocks are excellent insulators ("rock wool" is a commercially made insulator from rock materials), and it is difficult to find a place where sufficient heat flows into one area at a rapid enough rate to make it economical to recover. These sites do occur naturally in certain geyser and hot spring areas, but in general the problem has not been solved. However, drilling and experimental work are continuing, and we are learning more about the matter all the time.

The Pure Oil Company (now controlled by Union Oil Company of California), in association with others, recently drilled into a steam and hot water area near the Salton Sea in southern California. Not only do they anticipate producing steam from this area, but the brine from the wells is very rich in a variety of minerals, and this may possibly be one of the better "mines" for certain elements and compounds. The steam wells near Florence, Italy, were a problem at one time because of the large amount of sulfur in the steam. Sulfur in steam tends to form sulfuric acid which eats out the blades of the steam turbines. But a way was found to remove the sulfur economically, and now this liability has been turned into an asset. Thousands of tons of sulfur have been produced here, and many more will be extracted in the future. Sulfur being in demand as it is, this may be a profitable by-product of at least some geothermal energy developments.

Some local uses of sites of Earth heat concentration are interesting. One fellow had a hot spring on his property, and not far from him down the valley was a resort town with several motels. This was an all-year resort area, the motels catering to skiers in the winter, so need for heat was substantial. The chap with the hot spring made a deal with the motel owners to supply hot water to the motel heating systems from the hot spring. Except for occasional cleaning of the pipes, upkeep of this heating system is nominal, and the heat is free, compliments of old Mother Earth. The fellow with the hot spring has something even better than an oil well in his backyard, for, as already stated, the "reserves" of a hot spring or steam well are virtually unlimited, whereas an oil well eventually is pumped dry.

In some places, local residents have taken advantage of hot rocks in their backyards. In one area of Klamath Falls, Oregon, people have drilled wells a few hundred feet deep in their backyards and found temperatures quite high. Two public schools and an automobile agency there are also heated by water circulated down into the ground, and by means of heat-exchangers in the wells, the water is heated and returned to the building.

Future possible Earth-heat sites.

There are thousands of hot springs in the United States (Idaho, Nevada, Oregon, and California have perhaps the majority of them).[1] Also, many areas show abnormally high "geothermal gradients"—that is, the Earth gets hotter faster per foot into the ground than it does normally. All these places may be potential sites for the development of Earth-heat commercially. I am sure you will be hearing more about this field of research. The company operating north of San

---

[1] The U. S. Geological Survey recently published a comprehensive list of hot springs of the United States, and of the rest of the world: "Thermal Springs of the United States and Other Countries of the World—a Summary," U. S. Geol. Survey Professional Paper number 492, obtainable at the U. S. Government Printing Office, Washington, D. C., $2.75 a copy.

Francisco offered its shares on the market publicly several years ago. More such offerings can be expected.

Recently a bill was passed in the Congress clearing the way for this sort of endeavor. It gave the Secretary of the Interior authority to lease public lands for development of geothermal resources under terms similar to those of the Mineral Leasing Act. The first steam well in the Rocky Mountains was recently completed near Jemez Springs, just west of Santa Fe, New Mexico. At least two companies, with stock traded over-the-counter, are now engaged in developing Earth heat. These are Magma Power Company, and Thermal Power Company.

Summary.

Development of Earth-heat for commercial uses is already a fact in a number of areas of the world, and work continues on this problem. The technical difficulties are considerable but the potential for this sort of thing is very large. This may literally be a promising field for investment beneath our very feet.

THE SUN

Can you use sunlight which hit the Earth 300 million years ago? Sounds impossible but you are doing just that when you burn coal or use gasoline. You are releasing energy received from the Sun millions of years ago, and stored in organic materials. You are using "fossil sunshine." But this is energy from the Sun which has been transformed to a degree. Harnessing energy from the Sun directly has intrigued man for a long time but so far the results of trying to do so have been less than spectacular. This is a particularly frustrating situation because the Sun produces fantastic amounts of energy. It has been estimated that if we took all our available energy sources—coal, oil, natural gas, wood, uranium, thorium, and oil shales, and then extinguished the Sun, our total supply of these Earth-located energy fuels would be gone in just 3 days if used at the rate at which we receive energy from the Sun.

Vegetation absorbs and converts energy from the Sun which we can later use in the form of fuel but this is not a very efficient process. Some elaborate studies have been made to determine how much energy might be gathered directly from the Sun over various parts of the United States. One estimate showed that it was theoretically possible to produce from the Sun all of the present energy needs of the United States if an area of about 50,000 square miles in the Southwest was completely given over to collecting the Sun's energy.

However, at the moment fossil fuels (coal, gas, oil) are available to industrialized countries so cheaply, and in such quantities, as to eliminate, for the most part, the effective competition of direct use of the Sun's energy. Nevertheless, there are about 2 billion people on this Earth who are without electricity or the ability to purchase fossil fuels in quantity.

The immediate need for utilizing the direct energy of the Sun is in these less developed countries. But because of the fact that the more industrialized nations are not faced with any urgent need for capturing the Sun's energy directly, this has been an area of relatively neglected research. However, as markets abroad build up for solar energy conversion devices, research here will no doubt pick up. Use of solar energy is already a well-established practice in a few countries.

Small solar heating devices have been in use in Japan for many years. At a nitrate mine in the desert of northern Chile a distillation plant was set up in 1872 which used the Sun's energy. It operated for 40 years producing up to 6,000 gallons of water a day and was finally abandoned only because the mine was worked out. Other devices have been invented from time to time which, by the use of the Sun's energy, did such things as pump water, run a printing press, and light electric lamps. But except for the solar heating of water, these devices generally have not survived. Recently, however, Zenith Radio Corporation began marketing a portable transistor which recharges its batteries through sunlight. Research on this problem continues.

The U. S. Agency for International Development (AID) recently developed a solar-powered boat. The U. S. Army tested it and concluded that "the use of solar cells for propulsion of light-weight watercraft is feasible." The cells, mounted like a board on the bow of the boat, can generate about 150 watts in favorable weather, and can run electric motors which propel the boat at about 5 miles an hour, wind and current conditions being zero. The chief disadvantage of the boat is the high cost of the solar cells. (The Army said the device was "feasible" but because they were concerned with military uses, the matter of whether or not it was "economical" was not commented upon.) This is a circumstance characteristic of many solar energy-catching devices. Whereas the operating cost is low, the initial capital outlay is high —another reason why less developed countries find it hard to do much with the Sun's energy. By the same token, when such devices are developed and installed, they will offer a substantial outlet for investment capital.

For the present it seems likely that one of the more practical ways of using energy from the Sun in the United States is in special house designs which make use of lots of glass. Investing in glass would be a way, in effect, of investing in the Sun's energy—glass can capture sunlight, and retain it as heat in a room. (See section on GLASS.)

Some work has also been done on putting phosphor powders in paints and on papers. Clear daylight ranges up to 8,000-foot candles in the summer, but a room lighted at night with more than 100-foot candles is well lighted; the average room is lighted much less.. Only a small part of the day's sunlight would need to be stored to light a house at night by means of phosphorescent paint.

Also, some materials or combinations of materials do have the interesting ability (called photovoltaic conversion) to generate electricity directly from exposure to the Sun's rays. This is the principle of the cadmium sulfide coating on the mirror of a single lens reflex camera which reads the exposure directly through the lens—a very handy arrangement allowing you to take pictures even through a microscope without any guess work or using film in test exposures. Cadmium sulfide has an estimated efficiency of about 8% in this regard. Other materials include silicon (14% efficient), gallium arsenide (10%), cadmium telluride (4%), and selenium (1%). A good deal of research has gone into this area but so far the cost and efficiency of these photovoltaic methods is such that the generation of electric power is not practical except for use in generating power in space vehicles and satellites (where cost is no object). But research continues and it is a field worth watching.

Conclusions.

The energy potential of the Sun is enormous and it is hard to believe we will not be able to tap it more effectively than we are doing now. We are doing very little with it at the moment. Technology will find a way in the future to do much better, and money will be needed to finance these advances commercially. As in the case of much other research, however, I am inclined to think it will be the large, well-staffed existing companies which will make the advances. The simple problems have been solved. The complex ones remain, and to solve them takes high-powered and costly research. So follow what the larger companies are doing. Companies which have studied solar energy problems to a significant extent include General Electric, Westinghouse, Corning Glass, and Pittsburgh Plate Glass, among others.

Barring some spectacular break-through in solar energy research, it seems likely, however, that this will be a slowly developing field in the United States (and even less so in Canada because of a lesser amount of year-around sunshine). Again, the most obvious area of development is in the use of more and more glass in home and office construction to utilize the Sun's energy for space heating.

For a most interesting book on this topic, read "Direct Use of the Sun's Energy" by Farrington Daniels, Yale University Press, New Haven, Conn., 1964. Your public or university library has it, or you can buy a paper-bound copy from the publisher for $2.45.

FUEL CELLS

Science puts new words into our vocabularies almost daily. "Fuel cell" is a term recently appearing in ads in even some of our more popular magazines (Texas Instruments has been running such ads). A note about them is included here, not only because they are being brought to our attention, but also because they represent a most interesting and potentially important area of research. However, they are not a new idea, having been known to science for nearly 300 years.

Fuel cells convert chemical reactions directly into electrical energy. An ordinary dry cell battery is a fuel cell, but "fuel cell," as the term is commonly employed now, means a cell in which fuel is fed continuously into the system, whereas with a dry cell you use up all the fuel and eventually throw the cell away.

Fuel cells have a special attraction in that their efficiency in converting chemical energy to electrical energy has been experimentally as high as 70%, whereas the engine of your car is woefully inefficient in using gasoline. Fuel cells have the possibilities of very large scale development and application, and investors would do well to keep posted on them.

Fuel cells employ a wide variety of materials and involve several physical principles. Fuels which show special promise for us in fuel cells include petroleum, and for this reason among others, several of the larger oil companies have been, and are still, engaged in extensive research on this matter. Again, this is one reason why the term "ENCO" (ENergy COmpany) is the now-adopted title for one brand of petroleum products. Oil companies visualize the time when they will be selling substantial amounts of energy in other forms than they are today. In view of the high efficiency of fuel cells, their development to commercial use would be a very desirable situation from the long term point of view as it would enable us to stretch out our diminishing supplies of fossil fuels.[1]

Besides petroleum, fuel cells can be made to work with other materials. The oldest, yet most advanced, fuel cell is a hydrogen-oxygen cell. By this it is possible to make use of the Sun's energy to run a fuel cell, in that the photovoltaic principle of producing electricity (just described in the chapter on THE SUN) can be made to produce hydrogen from water by electrolysis.

Besides the major oil companies, General Electric and Westinghouse have studied fuel cells carefully and made working models. Allis-Chalmers Mfg. Company, Pratt-Whitney Division of United Aircraft Corporation, and Texas Instruments have also produced working fuel cells. You will be hearing more about them. Respected scientist and university president, Dr. C. C. Furnas, predicts, "Within the foreseeable future . . . a satisfactory and practical fuel cell will

---

[1] Fuel cells have another advantage over energy-converting devices such as the internal combustion engine, in that fuel cells do not produce products which pollute the air as does the gasoline engine. The rapid rate at which our atmosphere is becoming contaminated may dictate the use of something like the fuel cell to replace our conventional engines, out of sheer necessity for survival. (See comments of Dr. Morris Neiburger, meteorologist at the Univ. California at Los Angeles on this, as quoted in the chapter on AIR in this book).

be developed and universally used for the motive power for vehicles."

These comments on fuel cells, I trust, will give you a little background in the subject so when new developments are announced you can more readily interpret their significance. Then get further information from your broker and other sources, and invest accordingly. Fuel cells have a very large future potential.

Investing In Mines

I once bought 1,000 shares of stock in a mine for a total cost of $15. I was gypped, except for receiving several times $15 worth of experience. There is a "mine" in one of our Western states owned by a fellow who simply uses it as a tourist attraction, and one of the features of this mine is that the owner will sell you a genuine share of stock in it for 50 cents. It is a beautifully engraved certificate, and people buy it simply to have one share of stock in a gold mine—an attractive wall decoration, with their name on it.

This sort of thing is based on what seems to be almost an instinct in Man—to want to own a mine. I have seen this characteristic in many people and it is close to being a disease. I may have caught it myself a time or two. If it is a disease it seems to be one for which no antibiotic has been so far discovered, because the disease is far from being stamped out. Strangely enough, I have seen some very successful professional men who proceed in their own specialties with great care and thought, but who will put their money in the wildest sort of mining schemes with little or no investigation of the situation. When I say this instinct borders on a disease, I am not exaggerating, and it is also contagious.

The Alaska and California gold rushes, the more recent uranium boom, and many other smaller episodes, are evidence of this.

Get good advice.

When costs of digging all the holes in the ground are added up, it is quite likely that far more money has been put into the Earth than has been taken out of mines. Actually only a very small part of the Earth is productive. So far about 1,000 square miles have produced nearly all the mineral wealth of the United States. But there are many monuments to efforts to make much more of it productive— monuments such as a fine mill (a plant designed to crush and concentrate ore) which a small company carefully built, and now the mill is gradually falling to pieces, having never been used.

I was called in as a consultant to this company one summer as I had been doing geological mapping in the area of their mine and as a result got to be the local (and only) geological expert. The company had been organized by a group of farmers and they were as nice a group of people as I have ever met—and I did meet many of them one time when I came and explained the situation at a special (and rather sad) stockholders' meeting. I would have been glad not to have had that consulting job. The company had problems. They had purchased some mining claims and had invested a substantial amount of money in building a beautifully designed and equipped mill at the base of the mountain where the mining claims were located. There was only one difficulty. *There wasn't any ore!* This situation is sometimes known as putting the cart before the horse. A single piece of rock had been picked up—apparently a selected specimen that looked good. It had been assayed and it showed commercial amounts of the metal in question. My geological work showed that a few more pieces might be found to have this same metal percentage, but mineral deposits have to be measured in thousands or millions of tons to be commercial. This mine had no ore.

It may seem elementary to you from where you sit to say the company should have first done some drilling to outline the ore body if such was present, and to determine the quality of the ore and the tonnage. Only then, if the ore was good enough, would the mill be built. The fact was that on the basis of a single piece of rock, weighing no more than a couple of pounds, thousands of shares of stock were sold to individuals, and a first class mill was built by people who, in their own businesses, would get good advice and proceed cautiously. They caught "mine fever" and were carried away.

I have seen this phenomenon many times. It is not just the desire to try to get rich quick. This might be satisfied, one way or another, by a night at the gaming tables. It is a special sort of disease—people want to say they own a mine.

If you become involved in such a situation as this, by all means get good advice early. Contact a reputable geologist or mining engineer.

Good investment—or expensive wallpaper?

Some people have made fortunes buying mining stock. Cecil Rhodes—source of the famed Rhodes Scholarships—made his money in the mines of Africa. Individuals who originally, or very early, bought stock in the Sunshine Mine of Idaho obtained an interest, for only a few cents a share, in what became the largest single silver mine in the United States, a story told in greater detail later in this book. But for every one of these, there are 10 or perhaps 100 ventures which just became expensive wallpaper. Some saloon-keepers in Nevada and California have covered the walls of their bars with glittering, beautifully engraved, utterly worthless mining stock certificates.

I have such a piece of paper, framed and hanging on my office wall, to remind me not to do such things again. I can speak from experience on the matter.

Story of a "hot tip."

What happened was this: It was mid-winter in northern Idaho and I was a young professor teaching in a College of Mines. One day a student came in and said, "I know a fellow who knows a fellow . . ." and so on. The gist of this "hot tip" was that a mine existed high on a mountain side in northern Idaho. In the valley below, another mining operation had just cut a rich vein of ore which trended right toward this other mine, now covered with 12 feet of snow. The vein probably went right into the other mining property, but few people knew about this yet. This mine had been shut down for quite a while and the student said he could get me some stock at the fantastic low price of 1½ cents a share. How much could I lose? Just the idea of having 1,000 shares of stock for $15 was attractive—and think if the stock went to merely a dollar a share! We couldn't check on the geology of the area because of the snow, but we each bought some stock anyway. When the snow did melt we went back into the mountains and found a big fault—a break in the Earth's crust—between the two properties and against which the rich vein of ore terminated. Our mine was in the finest massive quartzite I have ever seen! Pure, unmineralized quartzite! If the market for quartzite goes up we are in. The only trouble is that whole mountains are made out of quartzite, and it is substantially harder than steel, and digging around in it lacks appeal. It is that rock they talk about when you hear the expression "hard as a rock."

In any case, how much could I lose, or did lose? I lost everything—which is a pessimist's way of looking at it. I prefer to think I only lost $15. But, as stated in the beginning of this chapter, I got my money's worth in experience. It's a pretty certificate, too, and the frame around it is well worth the 75 cents I paid for it at the dime store.

Assessable stock.

In regard to some mining stocks—especially the cheap so-called "penny stocks"—you should be aware of the fact that many of these stocks are assessable. The company can send you a bill from time to time, in effect. There is a sound reason for this. The stock, to get the mine started, is sold at some low price because evidence for the presence of a commercial mineral deposit may be rather flimsy. You can't know for certain what may be there until you do some thorough exploration work. So stock is sold and work begins. But money from the original sale of stock may run out before any good ore is found. You can either give up at this point, or you can put up more money and continue to explore. That rich vein may be just back of the present tunnel face one more foot! It actually might be! So the company levies an assessment of a cent or two a share on all outstanding stock. You can pay up, and if you don't your stock can be declared delinquent and eventually you forfeit your stock —it goes back to the company, can be sold to someone else, and you are written off the records as a stockholder. Many assessments are honest attempts to raise money for legitimate exploration purposes. If the company has good geological reason to believe further exploration is worthwhile, I am all for putting in more money. But sometimes the justification for more work is not good; occasionally I think the assessment goes primarily to pay "office overhead" which can be a fancy name for salaries and expenses of the company officials. Rules on this are a little loose, so if you buy assessable stock, be prepared to follow matters pretty closely and demand to have competent people recommend additional exploration work, if such is to be done at all. I would recommend you get pretty hard-nosed on this sort of thing.

Money can be made in marginal mines.

Most of the "penny stocks" are in marginal mines, but some money can be made in these, and has. It is largely a matter of timing. These circumstances in the past have commonly involved a situation where the mine had rock in it which was not quite ore at the current market price of the metal, but when the price went up a few cents, what was just rock one day became ore the next. The definition of "ore" is not geological; it is economic. An "ore" is an aggregate of mineral and rock material from which one or more metals can be extracted *at a profit*. The brown color of the dirt in your backyard is due to iron but that dirt is not iron ore. There are many mines which have large low grade mineral deposits. These mines open and shut depending on the ups and downs of metal prices. During wartime, many marginal mines made money, and "penny stock" prices rose in some cases from a few cents up to several dollars—and then went down again. At the right time, marginal mines can be a profitable investment. And there is always the chance that while the low grade ore body is being worked, something better may be discovered. It has happened.

Currently we have a good example of this sort of economic situation in the mercury business. The price of mercury has gone up very rapidly the past few years (more than tripled). What have been just holes in the ground are now mercury mines again. There is one such operation opening up just 50 miles south of where I sit in western Oregon at the moment. The lead-zinc Pine Creek District of northern Idaho is another such situation. I have seen this district boom and then collapse. It may boom again if prices for metals move up far enough to get ahead of mining costs.

Making money in these sorts of situations takes a lot of knowledge of particular mines and a fair amount of luck. Some mines are overcapitalized (too many shares of stock out). These have slim chances of ever returning much of a profit even with good metal prices. A few are reasonable situations. And there have been spectacular examples of mines once thought marginal which finally became big producers. One of the best is the Lucky Friday Silver-Lead Mine in the Coeur d'Alene District of Idaho which in 1940 sold for 5 cents a share, and which was eventually bought out by Hecla Mining Company in 1964. The equivalent of the initial 5 cent share of stock is now worth about $50! It is justly known as the "Fabulous Friday." This is the sort of true story which keeps people interested in these marginal "penny" mining stocks, and I guess I am no exception. A few situations have been fantastically profitable and the thought inevitably comes to mind that right now in the current list of stocks selling for a few cents a share there may be another "Fabulous Friday." There probably is.

Larger, established companies better for most investors.

In the long run, probably the most profitable course of action in investing in mining enterprises is to put your money in the bigger and already operating mining companies. They too, remember, have lots of low grade deposits which will become "ore" if metal prices move up. In the meantime these companies will still be making money and paying dividends to you from the better quality properties they are working.

Nevertheless, it is true that percentage-wise you can get a better run for your money in the cheaper mining stocks theoretically, because you start from such a low cost base. I have made some money in these low-priced situations, but in more cases than I would like to admit, my money is apparently still "running"—I haven't seen it since I "invested" it.

Stages of a mining boom.

My observations of several mining booms, notably the Timmins, Ontario, copper discovery in 1964, and the uranium rush in both the United States and Canada in the 1950's indicate a rather definite sequence of events, like this:

1. Initial report of discovery sets off staking of hundreds of mining claims in area, most located with little or no regard for the geology.

2. Stock is issued by many small companies just formed, to obtain money presumably for exploring and developing their claims. These are "penny stocks" and sell for a few cents to a dollar or so on issue. Some of these go up 10 or in some cases 100 times or more their initial offering price, moved chiefly by rumors. Most of these eventually drop to zero sooner or later. Stocks are issued in some cases where the company is never, or rarely heard of again after the first few months—this is especially true in Canada where rules have been less than strict (Canada is taking steps now to improve regulations). Unless you are on the location (and even then it is difficult to impossible) you cannot have more than a gambling chance of picking a winning stock. For most people it is better to stay out of this stage of the market but to stay out is hard, for the "get rich quick" psychology which sweeps investors in this situation is almost overwhelming. A good example of how fast cheap speculative mining stock can move at this stage of things came out of the Timmins copper rush. On rumors that the company had discovered a rich ore body, the stock of Windfall Oils and Mines, Ltd. rose from 56 cents to $5.60 in two weeks. When Windfall later announced negative results, the price of the stock *fell in one day* from $4.15 to 80 cents. If you were in Houston or Chicago or Los Angeles you would probably not be able to move fast enough to protect yourself in a situation like this.

3. Most of the smaller companies collapse after a few months, or at the most a year or two. Companies with good claims usually sell out to established mining companies. A very few companies have sufficiently large holdings to justify developing the property themselves. To show how things get concentrated in this third stage of a mining boom, it is noteworthy that a single set of mining claims assembled in Canada during the uranium rush are now reported to have more uranium reserves than all of the mines in the United States put together.

4. A few large, chiefly old established companies emerge from the mining boom with most of the newly-found resources. Only a small percentage of newly-formed companies survive even after the initial sorting-out takes place. After trying to run their own mines for a year or two many of these will also sell out to bigger established companies. However, once in awhile a large company can make a mistake and buy a property for more than it is worth. A classic example is the uranium mine found by the ex-electrician from Minnesota, Vernon Pick. This mine, in the Colorado Plateau, was eventually sold to Floyd Odlum as head of Atlas Corporation. The price was $7 million. The mine was exhausted after only about $2 million worth of uranium had been recovered. When asked how he felt selling a mine with only $2 million of uranium in it to Floyd Odlum for $7 million, Vernon Pick is reported to have replied, "He's over 21." Maybe you can do better than Floyd Odlum in picking winners among newly-discovered mines, but I doubt it.

When and how to get in.

It is my general advice that the best stage at which to get in on a mining boom, if you do not have good firsthand knowledge of it (and this would virtually mean you would have to be the geologist who made the discovery), is stage 3 —buy into an established company which chooses to put some of its retained earnings into carefully examined and considered new mining areas. Better yet, have investments already in established mining companies and wait until the companies buy into or discover new properties—which any good and alive mining company can and must do from time to time. Searching for new ore is a constant concern. Here it is important to buy quality. Buy good management and they will look after your interests. International Nickel seems to have been aggressive and successful along these lines, having found tremendous new nickel reserves in northern Manitoba while they were mining what is one of the world's great ore bodies in Ontario. Whether one should buy a giant company's stock or one of medium size might be a question. The relative value of an important new ore discovery will be greater to the earnings of a smaller company, of course. Balance this against the sort of exploration team the company seems to be able to attract and train, as evidenced from past exploration successes. But in any event it is worth repeating that the best way for most people to buy into new metal discoveries is to buy into established companies and let them do the exploration, the sorting, and the evaluation of properties which they may find or be offered by smaller companies.

Good companies are constantly diversifying and they

have the "know how" to do it right. To illustrate how a well-established company with a good exploration team is in a position to move into other natural resource areas than strictly their own initial interests, the case of the Humble Oil and Refining Company (subsidiary of Standard Oil Co., N. J.) can be used.

Wanting to know more about the geology of western North America, the Humble in the 1950's set up an exploration team of their own geologists and consulting geologists and undertook to explore a swath of land 300 to 600 miles wide along the west coast of North America from California all the way to northern Alaska. It was my pleasure to be associated with this project as a consultant. In the process of doing this work, some of the Humble men noted in flying over part of Alaska that they got abnormally high magnetic readings on their airborne magnetometers. Checking this on the ground, they discovered a very large though relatively low grade iron deposit. Result—the Humble Oil and Refining Company now has a potentially valuable set of iron ore claims in Alaska. The Standard Oil Company of Indiana (through their exploration subsidiary Pan American Petroleum Corporation) had almost the identical experience also in Alaska in 1964, ultimately staking 497 iron ore claims. Texas Gulf Sulphur, while looking for sulfide ore deposits in Canada, found a huge copper deposit near Timmins, Ontario; so good, in fact, that the stock price more than doubled in a very short time. Along with this went charges of "insider information," and one of the more spectacular law suits in recent years. This firm also shortly thereafter found a good phosphate deposit in North Carolina.

The point is this: *Well-established companies in the natural resource field are probably the best avenues by which the average investor can participate in new discoveries.*

Where mining stocks are listed and traded.

Most large mining companies, of course, have their stocks listed on the New York or American stock exchange, whose transactions appear in most papers. In Canada, the Toronto and Vancouver exchanges are principal mining stock exchanges (Montreal to a lesser extent), reports of which appear in the major and even in some of the smaller Canadian papers. An abbreviated list of Toronto Exchange mining stocks also appears daily in *The Wall Street Journal*. Canada has a great number of small mining companies, and these are chiefly sold over-the-counter; the most comprehensive list of these stocks is in an interesting newspaper called the *Northern Miner* published in Toronto (116 Richmond Street, West). We have no comparable paper in the United States. A month's subscription to the *Northern Miner* is an education in itself, and will give you at least a mild case of mine-investment fever. In the United States, most of the Western major papers (Seattle, Spokane, Salt Lake City, Phoenix, Denver, San Francisco, Los Angeles) have some coverage of regional and local over-the-counter mining stocks.

For investors who want to more thoroughly explore the field of mining stocks, an especially valuable publication is "Mining Stocks of the World," sold by Investor's Press, Inc., Palisades Park, New Jersey 07650.

Industrial Metals

Investing in a gold mine is the classic road to wealth, but there is much more money to be made, in total, by investing in industrial metals such as iron, copper, nickel, lead, and zinc. The demand for these metals is so great, and growing so fast for most of them, that the soundness of this field for investment cannot be questioned. *In the last hundred years we have used more mineral resources than the world has used up to then in all history.* And at present the rate of use is increasing.

The following pages present some basic facts about various industrial metals—demand, uses, and probable future growth trends. This information will give you a background for your investment thinking concerning these materials.

IRON

Cave man struggled up through the Stone Age; his descendants reached the Copper Age, then the Bronze Age, and then figured out how to smelt iron, and established the Iron Age. Now people are inclined to think we live in the Atomic Age. In a sense we do, but in the sense of what materials make up the backbone of our industrial civilization, we are still in the Iron Age and likely to remain so for a long time to come.

We are using iron at a very rapid rate. I can recall in my native Minnesota that before World War II the famous mine at Hibbing was a good-sized hole to be sure; but when I got out of the Navy after the war and visited Hibbing again, I saw a man-made Grand Canyon! The demands of the war emptied the high-grade iron ore from the area. The iron-mining companies were about to pull out of Minnesota when a tax concession law called the "Taconite Amendment" was passed in 1964, and companies could afford to remain and process the low-grade iron ore called taconite (it is about 30% iron as compared with hematite which is about 60%). Our industrial machine continues to swallow great quantities of iron, and there is no end in sight.

New deposits still being found.

Although this world has been rather thoroughly explored, and we are told to look out into space for new frontiers, it is interesting to learn that several new iron deposits of great size have been discovered in recent years. Two discoveries were made by oil companies, found accidentally while they were exploring for oil in Alaska (these have been mentioned in a previous section of this book). A third deposit was found in northern Baffin Island, third largest island in the world, located just west of Greenland. I have been on southern Baffin Island doing geological work in

August, wearing a winter coat and long underwear, and working during a snowstorm. With that sort of climate, the Baffin Island discovery, although reportedly of high quality, may not be ore under present economics. The shipping season may be too short, and the cost of maintaining a mining camp in such a cold and remote area would be high. Nevertheless, someday that iron deposit will be exploited.

Just as the deposit begins to be developed is the time, ordinarily, to invest. A number of years ago a high-grade iron deposit was discovered under Steep Rock Lake in Ontario. As the lake was being drained, I invested in the stock. When the mine came into production and earnings appeared, the price of the stock moved up to the level justified by the earnings, settled down there, and I sold.

The Baffin Island deposit may have the same sort of history. Keep it in mind.

Iron mining is basic business.

The iron mining business is fundamental. The material is bomb-proof and it surely is a good hedge against inflation as are most non-renewable natural resources. There is only so much iron in the world, and demand is increasing. Some iron mining companies just produce iron. Most mines, however, are part of a steel company's integrated operations. When times are good, the iron ore producers will do well; but when the cyclical steel business slows down, then the mines which are out on their own do less well than do the integrated mines. Most of the integrated companies will use only their own iron supplies when times are slow, and buy from other producers when things are better economically and the cyclical demand for steel is on the high side.

Investing in iron.

As just suggested, you can buy into an iron mine which is only just that, or you can buy into a steel company with big iron reserves. Keep in mind, if you consider smaller independent ventures, that the iron mining business involves millions of tons of ore to be commercial. I have seen some small iron mining ventures start which were impossible, and anyone taking 5 minutes to study the economics of iron mining would not have made such an investment error. A few exceptions do exist to the general rule that iron ore must be in huge tonnages to pay out. A company has been operating for some time a few miles west of Carlin, Nevada, on a small deposit. The ore is sold to the Japanese who presently have some of the most efficient blast furnaces in the world. The ore is located close to the main line of a railroad, also, so hauling is no problem. Even so, I am told the operation is marginal.

Summary.

Iron mining is a cyclical business. This makes for both buying and selling opportunities, but the business is fundamental so the long-term outlook is good. Iron mining is a low-profit high-volume operation, and ore reserves must be in many millions of tons to be significant. Shipping costs are a large factor, and location of the deposit is all-important. New iron mining companies are formed from time to time, but most of the new large discoveries are being made by existing mining companies or other firms in the natural resource field. Participation in the iron mining business through buying stock in existing and preferably integrated companies (firms which both produce and smelt iron ore) is probably the best way for the average investor to put his money into this natural resource.

COPPER

Copper has long been one of the most interesting and profitable metals in which to invest, and this situation is likely to continue. Copper tools have been used probably as far back as 6000 B.C., but copper is for the most part a metal of the Twentieth Century. The factor which puts such great emphasis on copper has been the development of our electric power systems and equipment.

Value of copper production in the United States is second in metals only to that of iron. The United States has for many years been the principal copper producer in the world, accounting for about a fourth of the supply.

As of recent years, about 25 mines produced about 97% of the domestic copper supply, and the 5 largest produced 52% of the total, according to the U. S. Bureau of Mines. We make the distinction here between mines and companies, for one company may own several mines. Kennecott, Phelps Dodge, and Anaconda (which has the world's largest copper reserves) produce about 75% of our domestic supply. Other companies include San Manuel Copper Corporation, Inspiration Consolidated Copper Company, Copper Range Company, Miami Copper Company (a division of Cities Service Company), and Magma Copper. Of these, Phelps

Dodge Corporation is the largest firm which has its production wholly in the United States (chiefly in Arizona). Other companies such as Kennecott, Anaconda, and American Metal Climax have interests also in foreign countries, notably on the African continent and in western South America. Copper reserves of these areas are very large, but the political situations tend to be unstable, and decisions as to whether or not to invest in companies with major foreign holdings are hard to weigh. However, by the same token, shares in these foreign-operating companies seem to fluctuate more widely in price than do securities of companies obtaining all or the majority of their copper in the United States and Canada; so speculative opportunities in these shares tend to come more frequently than in the stocks of purely domestic firms.

Trying to guess foreign political trends seems to utterly defy even our State Department; so perhaps one can do just as well if such things are ignored, and the basic facts of the copper industry used as criteria for investments. Nationalization of mines usually has not worked out to the best interests of the nation which does so (example: Bolivia). They can't eat the tin or the copper, and if mining operations don't run smoothly the countries suffer a substantial loss in income. One can probably make the assumption that some sort of a deal will ultimately be worked out whereby the copper can be mined at a reasonable profit for the company concerned. Combine this with the fact that copper is an exceedingly useful metal, demand for which is certain to continue in a strong growth trend, and you have the elements of a long-term, profitable business. There are fluctuations to be sure, but these can be buying and selling opportunities.

Copper is used by a number of industries having a

better than average growth rate. As stated, the principal push behind copper demand is the electrical industry. In the United States, use of electricity is predicted to increase about 7% annually for the next 10 years at least. In underdeveloped countries, as they get electrical facilities, the use of copper will soon be many times the present demand.

Types of copper deposits.

Copper is a relatively widely distributed element in the Earth's crust. Copper stains on rocks are common, as well as are copper deposits in small amounts, and hundreds of marginal mines and prospects are located in such deposits, especially in Nevada, Arizona, California, New Mexico, Colorado, and Montana. The famous and spectacular copper deposits of Northern Michigan were of native copper— copper not combined with other elements. This pure copper was worked by the Indians long before the arrival of the white man. Many of these deposits have been substantially mined out, and even the old mine dumps in some cases have been reprocessed a time or two.[1]

Dividends from this area are estimated to have exceeded $350 million at a time when the dollar was quite a bit bigger than it is now. Native copper occurred here in masses

---

[1] Two companies are still working this area, Calumet and Hecla, and Copper Range Company (which has done a really remarkable job in turning up new deposits and more efficiently mining already known lower grade ores). Mr. R. C. Cole, president of White Pine Copper Company (an affiliate of Copper Range) tells the story that the copper deposits in this area were reputedly first found by white men as a result of an accident—a herd of pigs fell into a prehistoric mine pit dug by the Indians.

up to several tons in weight. As an interesting sidelight, the mining of some of these pure copper masses was more difficult and less of a pleasure than the miners first anticipated. Blasting the copper only served to wedge the malleable copper farther back into the crevices of the rocks in which it occurred, and was a very frustrating experience.

Profitably mining ore with less than 1% copper content.

At the present time, much copper in the United States and elsewhere comes from what are called porphyry (poor-fer-e) deposits which are in masses of igneous rock broadly related to granite. In these the copper is widely disseminated, and cannot usually be seen by casual observation. It doesn't look much like ore. Very efficient mining, milling, and smelting operations now allow ores with a copper content as low as .4 of one percent to be mined profitably.

As the higher quality ores have been mined out, these lower grade deposits must be worked; but a compensating factor does occur in that the amount of ore increases markedly as one is able to handle lower and lower grade materials. That is, getting back to the definition of an ore—a natural mineral occurrence from which one or more metals may be extracted at a profit—as processes are devised to profitably extract copper from these low grade deposits, more and more rock can be classed as ore. The amount of low grade copper deposits is very large. Thus, as in the case of most metals, oil, and other natural resources, *technology is a prospector,* too, and can, in effect, locate new supplies, just as can the geologist who actually finds deposits previously unknown.

For most mining companies it is the combination that

wins. Their technical engineering staffs figure out how to use lower and lower grade deposits, and their exploration staffs at the same time search for entirely unknown areas of mineralization.

Avenues of investment in copper.

For the small investor, two principal routes to copper investment are open. The more obvious one is to simply buy shares in some of the big mining companies. Copper stock prices have fluctuated percentagewise more than has the price of the copper itself. There have been, in the past, some excellent times to buy, as general stock market conditions became temporarily depressed, or political unrest in some copper-producing country wherein certain companies may have large holdings makes headlines, scare investors away from stocks which may be affected. I am sure these fluctuations will continue in the future. In general, however, stocks in leading copper companies are regarded as good issues suitable for investment by banks, insurance companies, and other investment concerns. You are joining a high quality group of investors when you buy shares in the leading copper producers.

Buying into small mining ventures.

The other avenue of copper investing is to buy into smaller mining ventures, either via the "penny stock" route, or going into partnership with a few people in a small mine. This can be interesting, frustrating, profitable, expensive, or exciting, or a combination of all. Almost all the western regional over-the-counter stock exchanges in the U. S. and the exchanges in Canada trade in copper shares of smaller mines. New companies are formed, and initial stock offerings are made from time to time, too. Almost every copper-stained rock in North America at one time or another seems to have been staked by a prospector, yet a great new copper discovery was made in Canada (Timmins, Ontario) just recently. But even if every copper-stained rock on the surface has been examined, we are always faced with the tantalizing thought that just 6 inches beneath the surface somewhere can be the world's biggest copper mine (or any other kind of a mine, for that matter). This cannot be denied, and it is what keeps the old prospector going. Then, every once in a while, somebody comes rushing into town and claims he has just found that big deposit, and has a sample of copper-stained rock to prove it. Maybe he is right, and thus it goes. You can almost catch the mining fever from just reading these lines. You can see how contagious the get-rich-quick-by-investing-in-a-mine disease is!

A variation of this theme is that an old now-abandoned mine has some mineral showings, the ore vein has been faulted off but we now know which way it moved, or somebody was poking around at the end of the mine tunnel and discovered that a rich vein appears to be just a few feet back of the present tunnel face. Three thousand dollars of your money will enable the operator to strike it rich and split the million dollar profit with you. Again, who can say but what they are telling you may be right? They don't know either. It is a disease, I am convinced, but a fascinating one, and represents in many ways the spirit which built this country. A geological examination of the area will usually be reasonably conclusive but remember that the only real test is to dig or drill some holes. Gold—or copper—is where you find it.

Summary.

Copper is a basic commodity with a strong growth trend of demand for the indefinite future. Ore is now in sight which will keep the domestic copper industry in business for many years. However, the United States is likely to increase its dependence on foreign supplies. These foreign operations will need capital, and can potentially be a source of good investment profits; but the pressure for nationalization, higher taxes, and other factors of international politics are involved. It is likely, however, that agreements will continue to be worked out to allow companies to operate abroad. For some countries such as Chile and Peru, copper export is a very important source of foreign exchange. The history of nationalization of mines is such that a good many countries are reluctant to embark on that road 100%—Bolivia is an example of a country that tried it with disastrous results.

The growth of the electrical industry, especially, insures strong demand for copper for the indefinite future. Copper companies of quality are regarded as excellent investments even by conservative firms such as banks. New mining, milling, and smelting techniques will "discover" new ore deposits, in effect, and create investment opportunities. The uncertainties of foreign politics will also, from time to time, cause attractive investment situations to present themselves. If you invest in small copper situations, however, be sure to get some good advice as to just what the mine has in it.

Copper has no substitutes for many uses. It is in a basic and very strong position.

ALUMINUM

Aluminum is the third most abundant element in the Earth's crust, making up nearly 9% by weight. It has been known as an element, however, only since 1827, whereas many metals such as gold, lead, silver, and copper, have been known for thousands of years. Aluminum at one time was regarded as a precious metal available to only the rich. Napoleon III is reported to have had a tableware set made of aluminum.

Aluminum is an abundant metal, but it forms a very tight bond with other elements. Alumina (aluminum oxide) which is the source of aluminum, comprises about one-seventh of the Earth's crust. But the problem is to release aluminum efficiently and economically from this bond. The problem was solved, almost at the same time, by two men working independently. In 1886, a Frenchman by the name of Heroult, and an American named Hall found the key, and the Hall-Heroult aluminum reduction process came into existence. The key was electricity—again an illustration of the fact that energy is the natural resource which unlocks other natural resources.

Electrical energy is used in such vast quantities in the aluminum smelting process that aluminum ore is hauled thousands of miles to the energy sources—a circumstance which makes both the United States and Canada major aluminum refiners because they have the electric power, even though they are not major aluminum ore producers.

Use increasing rapidly.

Aluminum was first used as a substitute for other metals, but it has gained a position in our industrial scheme to the extent that the metals for which aluminum originally was regarded as a substitute, are now thought of as possible substitutes for aluminum. Aluminum technology seems to have been developing faster than that of many other metals, and aluminum is probably our fastest growing metal in usage. In 1885, less than 300 pounds of aluminum were produced in the United States. Using the newly discovered Hall-Heroult process, the United States produced nearly a million pounds of aluminum in 1895, and now production is close to $2\frac{1}{2}$ million *tons* a year.

Projected growth.

Production of aluminum in the United States has been estimated by the U. S. Bureau of Mines to exceed 7.5 million tons by 1975. *The annual increase in aluminum consumption is expected to exceed the growth of the Gross National Product by 2 or 3 times for the next 10 to 20 years, at least.* Aluminum is a strongly growing industry which offers an especially interesting situation for the investor in that major and minor technological break-throughs can theoretically be made, and some will probably actually be made in refining of the aluminum and recovery of aluminum for low grade materials, and in the uses of aluminum. For example, aluminum is very common, yet only one ore—bauxite—yields aluminum in appreciable quantities commercially, at present. If a way could be found to separate aluminum from other compounds cheaply (ordinary clay is an aluminum compound), the company having this know-how could be in a very profitable long term situation.[1] Also, the metallurgy of aluminum offers a great spectrum of possibilities. Each year it is utilized in more and more ways—one big potential field is the all-aluminum engine block, now actually produced by at least one company.

Investing in aluminum.

How can you invest in aluminum? Buying into aluminum companies (most of which have their own ore deposits) is the principal approach. Major producers are: Aluminum Company of America (Alcoa), Kaiser Aluminum and Chemical Corporation, Reynolds Metals Company, Harvey Aluminum Company, and Aluminium Ltd. (Note: Everywhere but in the U. S. the spelling is "aluminium" and pronounced "al-u-min-e-um"). All these companies have or have had crews out looking for aluminum ore—bauxite chiefly. Bauxite looks like (and is) a special variety of clay; the average person would probably not recognize it as an ore of a metal. A high-grade large bauxite deposit in the United States would be a welcome discovery as the United States imports 80% of its needs. Plenty of lower grade material exists in the United States, however, so we will always have aluminum—

---

[1] Since this manuscript was completed in preliminary form, the Anaconda Company announced a break-through on the problem of obtaining aluminum from clay, and is preparing to build a clay refining plant in Georgia. This is a discovery which could have very wide significance for the aluminum industry and is worth watching.

at a price. Currently, Arkansas produces most of the bauxite we mine in the U. S., from near a town by the same name, Bauxite, Arkansas. The bauxite there is a reasonably distinctive ore in form and color, and tourists frequently pick up samples to have as interesting souvenirs. Adjacent states, particularly, have been interested to see if they had some commercial bauxite deposits.

One day a chap walked into the office of the State Geologist of Texas (Director of the Texas Bureau of Economic Geology, to give his title correctly), and showed the geologist a sample of high-grade bauxite, stating that he had found it southwest of Austin. The State Geologist was much interested, naturally, and asked the man if he could find the spot again, and the fellow said he probably could. The State Geologist offered to drive the fellow back to the location immediately and they started out. An hour or so went by and the conversation had drifted around to the topic of aluminum ore resources around the world, and especially in the United States, with mention of Arkansas. There was a long silence on the part of the State Geologist's companion— finally the fellow said, "Come to think of it, I may just have picked this piece up over in Arkansas one time, near a little town, the name of which I forget." "Was it 'Bauxite, Arkansas'?" asked the State Geologist of Texas. "That's it," exclaimed his companion. The State Geologist brought the car to a screeching halt, turned around in the middle of the highway, and headed back for Austin. There was a very long silence after that.

Maybe you can do better in finding a new source of bauxite, but I rather doubt it, so finding an aluminum ore deposit is not the most likely way for profitable investment in aluminum. Buy the stocks of the aluminum companies. These companies are in a strong growth industry, where technological break-throughs on several fronts can make the industry even stronger, offering the chance for one company to overtake another. The race to see who comes out on top is far from over; in the meantime the ride is profitable.

Summary.

The aluminum industry is in a rapidly growing period, which will continue for at least 10 to 20 years and probably much longer. The principal ore of aluminum, until very recently at least, has been bauxite which is chiefly imported. However, discovery of a way to process aluminum-rich clays other than bauxite apparently has been made, and this type of technological break-through, as well as others, especially in the field of aluminum metallurgy, provide additional growth potential to the industry and are areas wherein one company may make spectacular gains relative to another company. The most satisfactory way for the average investor to participate in the aluminum industry is through buying the stocks of the major aluminum producing companies.

LEAD AND ZINC

These two metals are commonly found associated with one another in ores, and their price and demand have followed one another to some extent for a long time, so they are considered together here. Much of what has just been said about marginal copper deposits which are brought into production due to unusual price rises of the metal, also applies to lead and zinc. However, lead and zinc have historically occupied a relatively marginal position at best, compared with copper, chiefly because lead and zinc suffer from foreign competition more than does copper. Demands for lead and to a lesser extent zinc, have not shown the strong growth trend which copper has shown. Lead and zinc are more susceptible to substitutes than copper seems to be. Copper has the good fortune of being tied to the rapidly growing electrical industry; lead and zinc are not. At times, lead and zinc have been more or less a break-even mining situation with the profits in some mines coming from the small amounts of gold and silver associated with the lead-zinc ores.

In total, from 1925 to 1958, according to the U. S. Bureau of Mines, about 41% of the U. S. supply of lead came from domestic mines; about 34% came from reclaimed lead (scrap); and about 25% from imports. The tendency has been that domestic sources supply less and less of our requirements. This is not due to any basic shortage of lead and zinc in the United States, but chiefly due to the fact that foreign sources are cheaper because of higher grade ores and cheaper labor.

This situation is changing a bit, however. Recent increases in lead and zinc prices combined with the obvious continued growth in demand has encouraged several companies to develop new properties, chiefly in Missouri. Kennecott Copper Corporation is opening a mine in 1967 which will produce 60,000 tons of lead annually, as well as about 8,000 tons of zinc and minor amounts of cadmium and silver. American Metal, Climax and Homestake jointly, are developing another large property and building a 100,000 ton a year smelter. These developments and several smaller ones will probably make the U. S. nearly self-sufficient in lead by 1968.

The largest single use for lead is in storage batteries; the second largest amount is used in the form of tetraethyl lead compound (anti-knock) in gasoline.

Zinc is perhaps in a stronger position than is lead as to demand; use seems to be rising faster, there are fewer substitutes, and the recovery of zinc from scrap is not so easy as in the case of lead (only about 20% of our zinc is re-used zinc). At present, the United States supplies somewhat less than half of its own zinc requirements, and the trend appears to be one of increasing dependence on foreign supplies. Our neighbor to the north, Canada, has the largest known zinc deposits in the world. Consolidated Mining and Smelting Company of Canada has the world's largest zinc mine, the Sullivan Mine, in British Columbia.

Investing in larger companies.

There are a number of lead and/or zinc mining companies in the United States, including American Smelting and Refining, Anaconda, Bunker Hill, American Zinc, National Lead, St. Joseph Lead, and New Jersey Zinc (recently merged into Gulf and Western Industries, Incorporated). Also, as just noted, some very large companies such as Kennecott Copper with interests chiefly in other metals, are nonetheless involved to a considerable extent in lead and zinc mining. This illustrates the principle stated several times in this book, but worth repeating, that your investment dollar in any large mining or other natural resource company, will usually buy you an interest in a variety of natural resources. These companies have the technical staffs and the money to expand into these other areas and do the sort of costly exploration and development work it usually takes to find and bring into economic production the larger deposits.

Canada has some very important lead-zinc producers including Consolidated Mining and Smelting, Quemont Mining, Normetal Mining, and Hudson Bay Mining and Smelting. There is a host of others, and some of the smaller mines in Canada have very high grade deposits although not always extensive. The Vancouver and Toronto papers list scores of such companies which occasionally have made spectacular profits for investors in a very short time.

Both lead and zinc are widely distributed around the world, with Europe having good reserves along with the Soviet Union and Africa. Some of the richest deposits in the world are those in the famous Broken Hill District of Australia; more recently other large lead-zinc deposits have been found in Australia. It is possible for American and Canadian investors to buy stock in these Australian interests, and your broker can tell you how.

Investing in smaller situations.

The United States has a great many small more or less marginal lead and zinc mines, and as an investor you are likely to run into some of these situations from time to time. These smaller mines are usually more volatile situations, price-wise, than are stocks of the big producers, and they offer more speculative opportunities (more ups and downs) but not necessarily more profit in the long run, with some notable exceptions. At the times of metal price increases (usually during national emergencies of a military nature) many small mines spring out of the ground like gophers on a warm April day. Money can be made in these smaller companies, but sometimes it takes more luck than skill. Timing is all important. Nevertheless, there are lots of examples where stocks of these small companies have doubled or tripled or done much better than that in a relatively short time. In such cases, it usually is important that you be close to the situation. Buying "penny stocks" in small mining companies at a distance has lots of difficulties, and in general I cannot recommend it. A further sobering thought is that in the case of lead and zinc (and possibly all of mining in general) it is likely that more money has been put into the ground than has been taken out. I hope that some of the information and suggestions given you in this book will enable you to arrive at better than average decisions. Investment capital is needed, but in the right places.

As noted in the section on INVESTING IN MINES, stocks of many small mines are assessable—which is a mixed blessing. Some people think of it as buying into a mine on the installment plan, and if the mine pays off eventually, this is no doubt a good system. But it is worthwhile to do some hard-headed figuring on these situations. Find out what the reported ore reserves are and their quality, and if you can, find out *who* calculated them. Ore reserve estimates can sometimes be subject to widely different approaches, and who made the calculations is important. I have occasionally discovered that the president of the company did, apparently while seated in his office. In this case, his title should be "promoter" and not "president." Then look

up the number of shares of stock out (a surprising number
of small mines will have 5 to 10 million shares issued! [1]),
and figure out how much ore would be necessary to pay even
a small dividend. Remember that it is not the value of the
ore per ton in the mine that counts, but *what the net return
from the smelter is per ton.* Mine promoters glibly talk
about $10 a ton ore or some such figure, but if the smelting
and other costs are $9.98 a ton, the profit is a long way from
$10 a ton. Most small mines depend on custom smelters to
handle their ore. These smelters are usually part of some
larger company's operations. The company will smelt ore
for the smaller mines in the region on a service charge basis
charging enough to make a profit on the work, of course.
The custom smelter will make money even if the small mines
don't. This might be another reason to invest in the stocks
of larger mining companies rather than in the small situations. However, if you want to invest in small mines, I will
be the first to admit it is a fascinating enterprise. But I do
recommend you investigate the matter thoroughly and do
some careful figuring. If you are planning to invest any substantial sum in a small mine it will surely pay you to get a
competent geologist who is hired to be on your side and
look after your interests.

---

[1] The most remarkable example of an over-capitalized company
of which I have ever heard was called to my attention by a
geologist friend of mine, Dr. William Easton. Philippine Oil
Development Company (known as "Podco") ultimately had 693
million shares outstanding before it collapsed!

Summary.

Lead and zinc are not in the strong demand situation like that of copper, but use of both metals will surely continue to increase, more or less steadily. Zinc demand is somewhat stronger than that of lead. However, use of both is rising. Major companies offer the best investments for most investors but the great number of small mines offer a variety of interesting speculative opportunities from time to time. These should be investigated thoroughly, if you intend to place any considerable amount of money in them. Even if you invest a small sum, this should not be an excuse for not looking at things carefully. From considerable observation I am inclined to think that the most successful investor is one who does just as much checking on where he puts $500 as where he might put $50,000. Human nature being what it is, most people don't take this approach. The few who do are generally the few who finally come out on top.

NICKEL

Nickel is one of the most versatile metals. However, it is rarely used pure (as are copper and lead), but is commonly alloyed with other materials. With iron, for example, it makes stainless steel, taking advantage of one of nickel's most outstanding characteristics—ability to withstand corrosion. Uses of nickel are many and varied in industry. An increasingly large non-industrial use of nickel is in coins.

Belgium used nickel-alloy coins as early as 1860. Switzerland issued nickel coins in 1881. By 1939 over 100 countries were using nickel in their coinage. In 1965, because of the severe silver shortage, by act of Congress, the United States began replacing silver with nickel and copper in its coins.

Sources of, and demand for, nickel.

Demand for nickel has at times exceeded supply, and shortages occurred, for example, during the period 1950-1957. Currently, newly opened mines and expansion of existing mines are producing nickel to supply all requirements. Nickel is produced chiefly at three localities: Canada, Cuba, and New Caledonia (a French island in the South Pacific). Of these, by far the most important is Canada, and recent discoveries made in Manitoba reinforce Canada's number 1 position as a nickel producer. Very large deposits have been worked at Sudbury, Ontario, for years.

Only a relatively few companies produce nickel in any quantity, among which are International Nickel Company of Canada, Ltd., Falconbridge Nickel Mines, Ltd., and Sherritt Gordon Mines, Ltd., all in Canada. In the United States, the Hanna Mining Company has a marginal nickel mine near Riddle, in southwestern Oregon—the only one in the United States. There is little likelihood that the United States, currently the largest user of nickel, will ever be anywhere nearly self-sufficient in this useful metal. Good nickel deposits anywhere will surely find a ready market, and companies with exploration units searching for nickel have an interesting speculative appeal. Again we see the principle that it is the established mining companies which are likely to find new deposits, rather than newly formed companies doing this. The established mining companies have money coming in from their operations to finance their exploration staffs on a continuing and efficient basis. This is well exemplified by the fact that it was International Nickel Company of Canada, Ltd. which located the biggest single addition to nickel ore reserves in the world in many years when it recently discovered the northern Manitoba deposits.

Nickel is also produced as a by-product from certain other mining operations, but in general nickel is not found combined with other common metals in any sizable amounts. Rather it is associated with rocks which contain chromium and platinum. Accordingly, new nickel discoveries proper are going to be the sources for future supplies of nickel rather than from discoveries of other metals which may incidentally contain nickel. The supply of lead and silver, for example, may be substantially enlarged by a big copper discovery, but not so with nickel (some small exceptions to this general rule have occurred, chiefly in Canada).

Investing in nickel.

International Nickel Company of Canada, Ltd. is the world's largest nickel producer, and from the size of their reserves, they seem likely to remain so for some time to come. Investing in nickel involves consideration of a relatively few companies, several of which have already been listed. The business is steady and growing, and again North American investors are fortunate because they have on their continent the world's greatest deposits of an important natural resource in which to invest—just as in the case of coal, oil shale, and many other resources.

TUNGSTEN

Except for the fact that tungsten has been found in the United States at many localities, and numerous small mines have from time to time been opened, this metal might be merely treated briefly with the "minor metals," in this volume. But tungsten mines have claimed the attention and money of many small investors in the past, and a special word about the tungsten business is probably worthwhile because many small tungsten mines will be needed and opened again in the future. Right at the moment we are having a resurgence in tungsten mining in the United States after a number of lean years.

Tungsten is a very useful metal, chiefly in steel alloys where tungsten imparts qualities of extreme hardness and resistance to wear even at high temperatures. It is also widely used in electrical devices because of its high melting point.

Sources of tungsten.

China, North Korea, and Russia have the world's largest tungsten deposits, with China's having the lion's (or dragon's) share, by far. But tungsten is widely distributed, and the quality of the ore differs greatly from deposit to deposit. At times when the United States has been hard pressed for tungsten we have discovered we had quite a bit —at a price. This is the circumstance which has caused problems in the domestic tungsten mining business. I was once a consultant to a tungsten mining company. It had a variety of difficulties, one being that about the time it got ready to operate, the Government quit subsidizing tungsten by paying high prices for it, and the tungsten market took a tumble. Tungsten has had this history—wide fluctuations in price because of varying demand—and as international crises come and go and the Government decides to stockpile it and then not to stockpile it, tungsten may have this problem in the future. However, underneath all this is a steady increasing demand by industry; the military requirements have been what have caused the wild price gyrations.

Prospecting for tungsten.

Tungsten occurs in a variety of ways and in most of our Western states, particularly. A common occurrence of tungsten is where granite has come in contact with a mass of limestone. At this granite-limestone contact, the tungsten ore occurs, brought in by hot solutions from the granite when it was molten. Several tungsten ores have the interesting property of fluorescing under ultra-violet (black) light, and this makes the identification of ore easy. Also, it makes prospecting fairly simple. You can go out over a mountain side on a moonless and preferably also cloudy night (as dark as possible) and examine very large areas rapidly by means of a portable ultra-violet light. But there is one caution to be remembered: Many rattlesnakes are nocturnal, and a rattlesnake will fluoresce too. So be sure to poke your "tungsten ore" with a stick, and if it buzzes, don't stake a claim! An experienced prospector from Arizona once told me that in his state they had a variety of tungsten ore known as "Arizona scheelite" (scheelite is one of the ores of tungsten). But this "Arizona scheelite" was not an ore, although it fluoresces like tungsten ore. Scorpions fluoresce too!

Tungsten can be a small mine operation.

Tungsten has at times been a profitable small mine operation, run by just a few men. But relatively sudden and sharp fluctuations in the price of tungsten have been the small investor's nightmare with this metal. However, Free World supplies are dwindling and the demand is rising so tungsten is moving again into a relatively good position, perhaps on a more steady basis than before.

If you are considering a tungsten operation (becoming a partner or buying shares in a small mine) the first thing to do is to establish the quality and quantity of the ore. This usually can be done with a well-planned core-drilling program. This applies to all metals in rock. In times past, some Government money has been available to help on this —depending on how badly the country needed tungsten at the moment. But find out about the size of the ore body and its quality first. Be sure to pay attention to what impurities there are as some impurities make tungsten ores difficult to process. Get good technical advice. Usually you can get at least a small amount of advice free from the U. S. Bureau of Mines or your state geological survey. Some state surveys (Nevada, for example) will analyze a certain number of ore samples free for each citizen each year. These are not detailed analyses but still good enough to tell you if you have something worth pursuing or not.

Tungsten mining definitely can be for the small investor, but get good advice and proceed thoughtfully. There are no large tungsten mines in operation at the moment in the United States. Most tungsten we produce is produced by companies engaged also in other mining ventures (American Metal Climax, Molybdenum Corporation of America, New Idria Mining and Chemical, for example), and therefore it is hard to invest just in tungsten mining stock as such, unless you buy into a small more or less private tungsten mining venture. As the price for tungsten rises now again, these small mines are beginning to come to life, and over-the-counter mining stock brokers can usually tell you about some, if you inquire.

Summary.

Tungsten is in a basic position, and for some things tungsten has few if any substitutes. Demand is increasing. Many small deposits exist in a variety of grades. Capital will be needed to develop new sources, and some will make money for investors in the future, if the operations are based on good deposits and well managed.

MOLYBDENUM

Molybdenum is used chiefly as an alloy in steel, and gives toughness to that metal. It was this fact that the Germans used in the First World War which enabled them to build the famous cannon "Big Bertha"—110 feet long and weighing 142 tons. The tough molybdenum steel withstood the force of the blast which sent the 264-pound artillery shells into Paris 76 miles away. Molybdenum is also used in lubricants, in electronic equipment, and in catalysts.

How do you invest in molybdenum? That is probably the simplest natural resource investment question to answer —buy "Mount Moly." The commercial reserves of molybdenum in the United States are estimated to be more than 3 billion pounds. About two-thirds of this is in one deposit— "Mount Moly" as the mountain is called, near Climax, Colorado, under control of American Metal Climax, Incorporated. The United States supplies from 80 to 90% of the Free World's molybdenum.

Some molybdenum is produced as a by-product of other mining operations, notably copper. Both United States and foreign copper firms produce molybdenum, but the concentration of the Free World's supply of one metal in one deposit, as is the case of molybdenum at Climax, Colorado, is almost without parallel.

Demand for molybdenum will probably rise more or less with the rise in steel production, barring some unexpected new major uses which might be developed. American Metal Climax has been very aggressive in research designed to find new uses for molybdenum, as well they might—sitting atop the world's biggest single pile of that metal. Also, they recently have found what is reported to be a smaller but even higher grade deposit in the United States.

Knowing that it has so many of its eggs in a molybdenum basket, American Metal Climax has been diversifying into a wide variety of other mining enterprises, and also into aluminum refining. It has potash interests in the United States, and a 50% interest in rich iron ore deposits in northwestern Australia. The company also has a sizable investment portfolio of other mining company stocks through which it now controls about 10% of the world's copper production (largely in Africa). In recent years, about half of American Metal Climax's income has come from molybdenum, about a quarter from aluminum, potash, and other mining operations, and about a quarter in the form of dividends from other companies in which it holds stock (chiefly the African coppers). To my surprise, I recently learned that the company also has oil properties in the United States and Canada which, in 1964, averaged about 8,000 barrels a day production.

But the fact remains that American Metal Climax controls the largest molybdenum deposit in the world, so to buy into molybdenum, the most obvious way is to buy "Mount Moly"—American Metal Climax. There are a few other companies which produce molybdenum—Molybdenum Corporation of America [1] and Molybdenite Corporation of Canada, both listed on the American Stock Exchange, are significant minor producers.

MAGNESIUM

A striking ad of Dow Chemical Corporation shows an arm and hand thrust out of the sea holding an ingot of magnesium. Technology found a virtually inexhaustible sup-

---

[1] Although still a poor second in production, Molybdenum Corporation has a $40 million development at Questa, New Mexico, which currently produces about 10% of the Free World's molybdenum; it also has in California what is probably the largest single deposit of rare earths in the world.

ply of magnesium when a process was devised to obtain this element commercially from sea water. Even without this technological break-through, however, there was no shortage of magnesium, as it is the sixth most abundant element in the Earth's crust, and large deposits exist in many parts of the world. Extensive deposits exist in Nevada, Alabama, and in many other places in the United States and Canada. For all practical purposes, the search for magnesium is over. The United States is self-sufficient in this metal, for the indefinite future, and so is every other nation which borders on an ocean.

Magnesium is light, and a common use for it is as an alloy. It also is used in making high temperature-resistant materials involved in steel smelting (refractory bricks) and there are hundreds of other industrial applications of magnesium in a variety of compounds.

To invest in magnesium involves investing in a company, rather than financing any search for ore, or buying into a magnesium mine—although some mines do exist. Magnesium is an excellent example of how technology "discovered" a tremendous quantity of a natural resource. Dow Chemical Company has been the pioneer in this field, and for a number of years has operated plants which extract magnesium from sea water. Kaiser Aluminum and Chemical Company at Moss Landing, California, also has a plant doing this. A number of other companies produce magnesium and its compounds from land deposits. These include Basic, Incorporated (formerly called Basic Refractories), and a number of other refractory-making companies.

Magnesium use will probably grow at least as fast as the rate of growth of the United States economy as a whole; advances in magnesium metallurgy which find new uses for the metal may cause demand to rise somewhat faster than the GNP. The problem with magnesium is no longer one of supply, but of finding new markets for this very abundant metal.

BARIUM, CHROMIUM, LITHIUM, AND OTHER MINOR METALS

A large number of minor metals may be quickly disposed of from the viewpoint of the average investor as they are not abundant enough nor of sufficient economic importance as to constitute any substantial area for investment (although some individual situations do exist, and some will be pointed out). However, I mention them here because they do have a definite place in our economy and we need them all in small quantities. You may encounter an opportunity to invest in a mine or in a company producing one of these minor metals, and a few lines about some of the more important ones are included here to make the book more nearly complete.

Barium.

Barium in various forms is used in a number of chemical processes, in glass making, and in paints, among other things. But the principal use of barium is in the form of barite, a barium sulphate, which is used in drilling muds to give them weight, for barite is quite heavy. The drilling mud is "weighted" by increasing the amount of barite in it, and in this way the pressure in the well bore can be controlled. As nearly 90% of the barite used in the United States goes into this one industry, barite production is tied very closely to oil well drilling activity, which has had some fairly wide fluctuations.

The two principal producers of barite are the Baroid Sales Division of National Lead Company, and Magnet Cove Barium Corporation, a subsidiary of Dresser Industries (which is a leading supplier of oil well and drilling equipment). New uses for barium will probably continue to be found, and the trend of consumption is firmly, but at the present time rather slowly, upward.

Chromium.

Chromium has a wide variety of minor uses, but chiefly it is used as an alloy of steel. The United States must import nearly all its chrome needs, as domestic supplies are small. A large source in the United States would be welcomed. The Government has at times stockpiled chrome because of its strategic use in making certain types of specialty steels. The Government has also encouraged exploration for chrome in the United States by sharing costs with private industry, but so far no major new ore discoveries have been made. The United States does have some low grade deposits, however, which can be used if circumstances demand, and cost was a secondary consideration.

Increase in production of stainless steel will mean increased need for chrome, and the outlook is for a relatively tight market in chrome for the indefinite future. The Soviet Union is reported to have the largest chrome deposits of any one country, although Africa as a whole has larger reserves. Turkey also has substantial deposits. American Chrome Company has a mine at Nye, Montana, which appears to be the largest United States reserve. Other chrome sources are scattered among more than 20 countries.

Lithium.

This is the lightest of all metallic elements; it is also one of the more important of the minor metals. Its principal use in the past has been in glass compounds and in certain types of storage batteries, and in lubricants. A number of new uses are being found for it, however, and its future is promising.

Lithium is produced in small quantities from a variety of sources including certain types of rock deposits, and from the brines of Searles Lake, California. Several firms produce lithium, but most of these are subsidiaries of companies whose basic business is in other types of raw materials. However, one company, Lithium Corporation of America, was set up for the production of lithium. This company is listed on the American Stock Exchange, and the stock price performance at times has been spectacular, but its dividend record has not. Recently, Lithium Corporation and a German firm agreed on a joint venture to produce magnesium, potash, and other minerals from Great Salt Lake. Lithium Corporation holds about 43,000 acres of land in this area, so the company is diversifying, which will probably give it more stability, and improve earnings.

Lithium consumption is increasing, but the industry historically has faced marked fluctuations in demand—which probably accounts for why Lithium Corporation is trying to get into production of other minerals, also.

Cadmium.

Cadmium sulfide, in photovoltaic cells, has ability to convert light energy directly into electrical energy. At the present time this phenomenon is chiefly used in connection with photoelectric cells of light meters and cameras, and in other small pieces of electrical equipment, but cadmium's unusual property could possibly result in discoveries of new and more extensive uses for this metal. Cadmium is also used in various alloys, in chemicals, batteries, pigments, and in electroplating.

The United States is the world's principal producer and consumer of cadmium. Cadmium is obtained solely as a by-product of zinc mining; there are no ores of cadmium as such. To buy cadmium, buy zinc deposits (for example, Bunker Hill Company). Canada (world's largest zinc reserves) and Mexico appear to have more cadmium than does the United States, but, although these countries produce some cadmium, neither seems to make the effort to recover it as is done in the United States. If cadmium became in greater demand, however, zinc mining companies in these two countries would be the potential major suppliers. In Canada, Consolidated Mining and Smelting Company, Ltd., would probably prove to have the largest cadmium reserves, as it operates the world's largest zinc mine.

Cobalt.

Cobalt is a relatively rare element, but is rather widely distributed in the Earth's crust, chiefly in association with ores of copper, silver, lead, zinc, and nickel. Cobalt minerals are rarely found in sufficient quantity by themselves to be mined, and therefore cobalt is largely a by-product of other mining operations. To invest in cobalt, mainly one would buy into companies which had large lead, zinc, or copper deposits.

Most cobalt used in the United States goes into steel alloys, especially high-speed cutting tools. The outlook for cobalt is for increased demand, more or less related to expansion of steel production, although new uses for cobalt can be expected to increase this rate slightly. It is improbable that the United States, which is the world's largest user of cobalt, can supply much more than 25% of its own needs from now on. More and more cobalt will have to be imported, although it may be that we will eventually get all our cobalt from the sea floor (see chapter on THE OCEANS —LAST GREAT FRONTIER ON THIS EARTH).

A good cobalt deposit in the United States would have an excellent future. The largest known cobalt reserves are in the Congo. Canada has extensive deposits, and Canadian copper, lead, zinc, and other mining companies will be sources of supplies, but cobalt is not likely to be a very large factor in such company's earnings in total.

Mercury.

Mercury has been known for more than 2,000 years; it is in increasing demand today and the price of mercury recently has gone up very sharply. Mercury is sold by the "flask"—a unit which weighs 76 pounds. Currently the price of a flask is about $360, up from $80 in 1949, and $229 in 1958 (New York prices). Mercury is widely distributed in the world with principal deposits in Italy, Spain, Soviet Russia, Yugoslavia, Canada, and the United States. New Idria Mining and Chemical Company (listed on the American Stock Exchange) is a major U.S. producer. Because of differing grades of ore in various parts of the world, and the varying costs of production, the producing patterns tend to shift geographically from time to time. At the moment, mercury mining, because of the price increase in mercury, is having a strong resurgence in the United States where deposits occur chiefly in California, Nevada, Oregon, Idaho, and Alaska. Mercury comes in the form of a pretty pink-red sulfide called cinnabar. It is easy to recognize in the field. Also, pure elemental mercury can easily be obtained simply by heating the ore, vaporizing the mercury, and then condensing it. One, two, and three-man operations have been common in the past, and with a good deposit of cinnabar, some of them have been highly profitable.

With the ease of recognizing mercury ore and recovering mercury from it, however, comes a marked disadvantage—at least to those people working the mine and retorting operations. Mercury poisoning is easy to get, and a variety of results are evident from it including having your skin turn green and your teeth fall out. But mercury can be a small yet profitable operation, and right at this moment in the United States a number of small mines are making money. A mercury mine was just opened about 50 miles from where I am writing this in western Oregon. If the price of mercury continues to rise, or simply remains at this high level, many more mines will be opening. Mercury can be for the small investor, but be sure the green color you get from the venture is only on the dollar bills you pocket. Mercury demand will stay high.

Tin.

Tin ranks fifth in world output, among non-ferrous metals, with only aluminum, copper, lead, and zinc ahead. But tin is not for the average investor, chiefly for political reasons. The United States has virtually no commercial deposits of tin. They occur principally in Malaya, Indonesia, the Congo, Thailand, China, Bolivia, and Nigeria. Any student of newspaper headlines will note that tin occurs where politics are in more than ordinary turmoil. Fortunately for the United States, and unfortunately for the tin-producing countries, tin can be replaced by many things for most uses. (American Can Company recently developed a tin-free all-steel can.) Because of this, the demand for tin will probably expand less rapidly than will our economy as a whole. Tin is a good example of where politics, not economics or the basic geology of the material, dominate a natural resource development to its detriment. I am not enthusiastic about such situations, from having lived abroad and seen these circumstances firsthand. There are degrees of this problem. In the case of copper, I think the countries generally will have the foresight to see that production is maintained, but I am not so confident about most of the tin-producing countries.

Titanium.

This metal, in dioxide form, is used chiefly in paints, as a pigment because of its extremely good hiding power, but other uses for titanium are expanding. The net result is that our use of titanium is increasing faster than our Gross National Product. The United States, India, Australia, and

Norway are among the principal producers of titanium ore. Some large companies have subsidiaries which are concerned with producing this metal (National Lead Company, for example), but a number of smaller companies have mined titanium ore from time to time also. Titanium will be in strong demand for the foreseeable future and any large deposit discovered should have a good future for investment if the venture is well managed.

Vanadium.

Vanadium is used chiefly in steel alloys, making them exceedingly hard and tough. This metal is obtained largely as a by-product of uranium ore mining. The United States is both the principal producer and consumer. Vanadium use will go up with the growth of the steel industry, principally, but vanadium can be replaced in part by other alloying metals. It offers a limited investment outlet, as far as present circumstances and the reasonably foreseeable future are concerned.

Other metals.

We could go on, metal by metal: Antimony, beryllium, bismuth, cesium, columbium, gallium, germanium, hafnium, manganese, radium, rubidium, selenium, tantalum, thallium, zirconium, and we have skipped a few. But generally, as we have seen, these minor metals are either produced as a by-product of a larger major metal mining operation, or they occur chiefly abroad and under circumstances (mostly political) which make it inconvenient or unrewarding for American investors to put money in such things. Or they occur in such small deposits or are used in such small amounts, or both, as to make it unlikely that the average investor will ever come across them. They do not constitute a very significant investment outlet, in general. A few of them could be worthwhile situations even though relatively small, if good deposits are found.

Rare earths.

Molybdenum Corporation produces europium oxide, recently in very strong demand, and its Mountain Pass, California, mine is probably the largest single deposit of rare earths in the world. Rare earths in general have shown more promise than profit for the investor. New and spectacular uses always seem to be "just around the corner." However, gradually more uses are being found for them, and there is always the possibility of some new large demand developing for one or several of them because of a newly discovered industrial process or development of new equipment using a rare earth. As noted, europium is an example of one rare earth which did recently come into its own. This material gives a 40% improvement in the brightness and trueness of colors in a color TV tube. In 1961, Molybdenum Corporation shipped 500,000 pounds of rare earth oxides, and in 1965 it shipped 14 million pounds. This increase was mostly due to the demand for europium, and it resulted in a doubling of earnings per share just between the years 1964 and 1965.[1]

---

[1] Molybdenum Corporation now has a process which can produce 99.9 percent europium oxide concentrate. Previously, this sold for as much as $1,500 a pound, but Molybdenum Corporation's process used at their $1.5 million plant at Mountain Pass (east San Bernardino County) enables them to sell europium

Other such developments could occur, so the rare earths are worth watching. In the meantime, familiarity with them will at least give the investor an impressive vocabulary while he waits for them to become profitable. They are: Cerium, dysprosium, erbium, europium, gadolinium, holmium, illinium (also called promethium), lanthanum, lutetium, neodymium, praseodymium, samarium, terbium, thulium, and ytterbium. Scandium and yttrium are close to but not strictly in the rare earth group. Research Chemicals division of Nuclear Corporation of America is the chief producer of these two elements. Yttrium, like europium, is used as a phosphor in color TV tubes. Rio Algom Mines, Ltd., of Canada, is also developing a large yttrium deposit.

If you are offered the opportunity to invest in these minor metals and rare earths, it might be well to get expert advice on what the future appears to hold, as they are a highly specialized situation usually. If you write to the U. S. Bureau of Mines, they can tell you the current supply-demand situation on these metals, and will probably know of latest uses for them.

---

oxide for about $600 a pound, and even with this marked cut in price, the earnings of the Company have increased substantially. This is an excellent example of how technology, in effect, "found" a new mineral deposit, by improving recovery processes, making more rock into "ore," and also cutting the price to the point where increased demand at this lower price more than compensated for the cut in price. This principle applies to many of our natural resources and herein lies one of the greatest areas for fortunes to be made in the future, in my opinion.

Gold, Silver, and Other Precious or Popular Materials

Gold was probably the first metal to be picked up and prized by Man and he still picks it up and prizes it. Gold was very early used as a medium of exchange, and it remains a substance which nations that may not agree on anything else can agree upon as to its value and thus conduct trade. (Of course, it must be recognized that the supply of gold is not sufficient on which to base all trade; much trade is not based on gold, but gold can be and frequently is the medium of exchange that nations resort to when they cannot agree on other forms of exchange.)

Silver is a very useful industrial metal, the demand for which currently exceeds production, and this has caused trouble in connection with our own silver coinage system in the United States. It, like gold, can serve as a medium of exchange—a common denominator by which diverse nations can conduct trade.

Platinum, like silver, is a useful industrial metal, and ounce for ounce is much more valuable than gold, but is not abundant enough to become a medium of exchange except in rare circumstances.

The use of gemstones, like the use of gold, seems to predate recorded history. The urge to have gemstones appears to even precede Man, for our western pack rat collects brightly colored pebbles, as do certain birds. Wives and girl friends do too—I am told.

Gold, silver, and other precious materials have long held a special fascination for Man. Although not so large a field for investment as unromatic resources such as lead, coal, copper, or iron, most of these rarer materials have a very solid niche in our economic and social systems, and every investor wants to know something about them. People also like to collect agates and other relatively common but showy minerals, and rocks. This circumstance has some small but locally important investment potentials especially suited to individual enterprise and development. Some suggestions and examples relating to how these popular Earth materials might be profitably worked into a small business or sideline are presented in the following pages.

GOLD

"He found a gold mine" is the common expression used to describe any exceptionally profitable situation. Naturally, everybody would like to own a real gold mine—the "type example" of a gold mine. But the gold mining business has led a hard life and one should approach this area of investment armed with considerable knowledge of economics and politics.

Gold is currently subject to price control in the United States, and has been since 1934 when President Roosevelt pegged the price at $35 an ounce. Since that time, in the gold mining industry, average wages have nearly quadrupled, the prices of supplies have gone up substantially, but the U. S. gold price remains the same. Furthermore, during the Second World War, all gold mines in the United States were shut down as non-essential industry, and re-opening them was a matter of considerable expense. In the meantime, the investors got nothing.

On the other side of the (gold) coin is the fact that gold is the one material which all nations can and will use as a last resort as a medium of exchange. Nations may not trust each other and their currencies (frequently for good reason), but gold is the common denominator, and trade can be conducted using gold as the grease to lubricate the wheels of commerce.

Politicians are fond of minimizing the usefulness of gold, and as countries live beyond their incomes and their currencies depreciate, it is politically convenient to ignore gold as a standard of exchange, or as a base for currency. But my firm opinion is that gold is not likely to go out of style; somebody will always want it—at some price. A good gold mine is worth having. The problem is to operate it economically. Gold has been prized for thousands of years; historically it has almost always increased in value over any reasonably long period of time. It has also had a side value, by the way, in that the search for gold has helped in pushing back the frontiers of new lands through "gold rushes." Also, alchemists seeking to make gold out of some other base metal never turned the trick, but in trying to they learned a lot about chemistry. Gold is still eagerly sought after, and I see no change in this situation.

But good gold mines are scarce. The United States has only a few—the Homestake Mine being the largest and most successful by far. A small but relatively high grade deposit is being mined near Republic, Washington, by Day Mines, Inc. Because it is a rare occurrence to have a large new gold mine opened in the United States, mention must be made of the development by Newmont Mining Company of a gold mine northwest of Carlin, Nevada, which I visited in its initial stages during the summer of 1964. When in full operation it is expected to turn out about 200,000 ounces of gold a year, at which time it will be exceeded only by Homestake in production.

Interestingly enough, some prospectors are still panning Western streams, and recently I heard of a situation in California where several men for a number of years have been coming into a remote canyon by helicopter. They spend 3 months there panning for gold, and the rest of the time they live elsewhere and seem to have plenty of money with which to enjoy life.

Undoubtedly some gold placer deposits (a placer is a sand or gravel deposit from which metal or metals may be extracted at a profit—more or less an unconsolidated "ore") remain to be discovered. Not long ago a young fellow showed me a couple of nice gold nuggets he had gotten out of a remote creek in the Klamath Mountains of Oregon (or so he said). But by and large placer mining (except perhaps in Alaska) is a rather limited situation.

To return to gold mines proper, Canada has had many more gold mines (some relatively small, however) than has the United States, over the years; but they too are running into hard times. Labor costs go up and as ore gets deeper or leaner, or both, some distinguished old mines have been closed. Recently a large cave-in caused management to review the situation at one mine and they decided not to re-open. South Africa is the principal gold-producing country, accounting for about twice as much annually as the next two leading countries combined. Following South Africa are Russia, Canada, the United States, Australia, New Zealand, and the South American countries (not necessarily in that order), with minor amounts coming from a wide variety of other places.

There certainly is such a thing as "gold fever." Gold remains a magic word and the investor must be wary he does not get infected and let the fever destroy his good judgment. Gold is fairly widely distributed but in minor amounts so that you can get lured into situations which are marginal, rather easily. Most of the streams of the Sierra Nevada of California will show "colors" in the gold pan. Small flecks of gold occur in many quartz veins (gold is commonly associated with vein quartz). I have had many an old prospector in Alaska pull out a worn, dirty piece of quartz from his pocket and, with a magnifying glass, have me examine it. It contained native gold, and if the vein from which the specimen had come was 50 feet wide and 1,000 feet long, and 500 feet deep, it might pay to move in equipment and go to work, but most of the specimens come from little quartz ledges here and there which have no great extent and are non-commercial.

I do not deny that good gold mines will be found in the future. I surely hope so, and some will be. I hope you will be the one to invest in such a successful situation. But I have seen a number of these ventures organized in various ways, stock sold, and then they fail. The problem frequently is that people are so eager to get in on a "gold mine" that they are willing to invest their hard-earned money far sooner than they have facts enough to make such a decision logically. They want to see a good gold deposit so badly that they hypnotize themselves to some degree.

My advice is to avoid unseasoned gold mine ventures unless you are willing to spend some money for good technical advice—having a mining engineer or geologist examine the situation thoroughly for you. On the other hand, well established gold mines are regarded as among the more conservative investments—although the fixed price of gold is making it difficult for mines in the United States to continue operation. The exciting speculative elements of investing in a sound gold mine lie chiefly in two possibilities—the chance the price of gold will be raised, and the possibility that in the course of mining operations, a big new rich unsuspected ore deposit may be found. Or the company may have teams of geologists out looking for other good prospects, and they may turn up something.

Africa—the continent with most of the gold.

Africa is the world's largest gold-producing area. One way investment in gold can be made there is by buying into some of the so-called "mining houses." These companies provide financial backing for gold mining ventures, and as a result frequently get some of the mine stock. They also provide consulting service (technical advice, geological and geophysical work) and therefore are in a position to know firsthand how the various companies are doing and what their prospects are. If you buy into an individual mine, eventually the mine will become exhausted, even while you hold the stock; and if you haven't set aside part of your dividends as return of capital to replace the stock by buying into another situation, you will end up with nothing.[1] The "mining houses" anticipate this and shuffle their holdings accordingly. The largest of these is Anglo American Corporation; others include Rand Mines, Ltd., and Consolidated Goldfields, Ltd. These companies, by the way, have other interests besides gold. There are also some companies which are chiefly gold holding companies such as Orange Free State Investment Trust, and West Rand Investment Trust (both of which are part of the Anglo American group of companies) and West Witwatersrand Areas, which is part of the Consolidated Goldfields group. American-South African Investments (listed on the New York Stock Exchange) is a closed-end investment company holding African gold stocks.

I take the time to present these details to give you some "feel" for the situation, and when you go to your broker you will have a background in the matter. Here is where a good brokerage firm can certainly help you because they have the facilities and the information by which to sort out these situations and give you an opinion on their relative merits. It is somewhat of a maze for the average investor.

---

[1] For the record, the gold mine which appears to be perhaps the largest gold mine the world has ever seen is Western Deep Levels, Ltd., of South Africa, whose total expected production is now estimated to be about $2.4 billion. However, because of its fame, the price of the stock seems to have moved up, at least at the present time, to the point where it is rather fully valued, as justified by annual earnings.

Some gold-producers in the United States and Canada.

Principal gold-producers in Canada include Campbell Red Lake, Dome Mines, and McIntyre Porcupine, all listed on the New York Stock Exchange, and Giant Yellowknife (controlling interest held by Falconbridge Nickel Mines) on the American Exchange. Dome Mines and Campbell Red Lake are one company to the extent that Dome Mines owns 57% of Campbell.

McIntyre Porcupine Mines, Ltd., holds a large portfolio of other mining company stocks, so you are buying much more than gold when you buy this company's shares.

Homestake Mining Company, office in San Francisco and mine in the Black Hills of South Dakota, is the leading United States gold-producer [2] but it is interesting to find that as of 1963, at least, this company received 57% of its profits from the uranium mining business. Because of the Government-fixed price of gold at $35 an ounce, and increased labor and material costs, during the past 10 years Homestake's profit has dropped from $12 an ounce to $7 per ounce of gold mined. Uranium has helped but is based on Government contracts which are due to expire before long (although they could be renewed, of course). Homestake is trying to diversify and has brought a brick plant

---

[2] Kennecott Copper Corporation is the nation's second largest gold-producer, recovering gold as a by-product of their copper operations. It will be pushed into third place, however, when Newmont Mining Company gets its Nevada operations in full production.

in the San Francisco area, and is laying plans for joint ventures with other companies in such things as a lead-zinc mine in Missouri (with American Metal Climax). It has a 25% interest in an Australian iron deposit, and it plans to enter the potash mining business in Saskatchewan.

These non-gold mining activities on the part of Homestake illustrate a common circumstance with mining companies—the title may be misleading. They may retain the name of "gold" or "silver" mine, or be thought of as a gold mine by the public, for historic reasons; but as the companies are forced by economics, politics in unstable countries, or by depletion of the ore body (or any combination of these circumstances) to do other things than originally planned, the true character of the company changes even if the name does not.

Hidden values in mining companies due to stock holdings.

Hidden values develop under these circumstances at times—a simple example being several companies in the past which have evolved to being mine holding companies. They bought stock in other going mining concerns as their own mines faded. Sometimes if you add up the value of all the stocks in a company's portfolio you will find you can buy $100 worth of stock for $75 or some such good discount. This may be a cheaper way of buying into another mining company rather than buying the stock of the individual company directly. The annual report of the mine-holding company will usually list the amount of stock held in other companies. The M. A. Hanna Company is a mine-holding company, and when it was traded recently at 38 its assets were about $62 a share.[3] As previously stated, McIntyre Porcupine also has a diversified portfolio of mining stocks, as does American Metal Climax. A number of other such situations exist. Your broker can tell you about them.

Gold, politics, and nations.

The "great gold debate" goes on and on, as everyone sees just by reading the daily paper. Politicians try to discount the importance of gold in our currency systems while at the same time great nations vie with one another for their gold supplies. France recently raided Fort Knox this way. As a result, stocks in gold-producing companies have had some rather wild price gyrations, as devaluation rumors (of the pound, the dollar, et cetera) circulate, and I am sure we have not seen the last of this.

What is gold worth?

There is one aspect of this whole gold matter which must be squarely faced by investors. Some economists claim that the dollar (which buys gold at $35 an ounce) is what supports gold rather than gold's supporting the dollar. Basically, it is implied, what supports the U. S. dollar is the industrial might of the United States, the value of its lands, et cetera. This argument further states that if the U. S. Government

---

[3] Since the initial draft of this manuscript was completed, the M. A. Hanna Company recommended to its stockholders that it be liquidated. The price immediately moved up sharply, and closer to its asset value.

did not buy gold at $35 an ounce, the price would go down appreciably in a free and open market. If this should happen, of course, the gold mining business would be in bad shape. I don't know what would happen if gold were not bought by the U. S. at $35 an ounce. But it is true that industrial uses (and jewelry uses) of gold are not great, and these demands might not support gold at $35 an ounce. Gold in the past has, from time to time, sold for more than $35 an ounce, but at the time I am writing this right now, gold is quoted on the London market at $35.16/ounce. How much this represents a true free price of gold and how much it represents the support price paid by the United States is an interesting question. Perhaps, by coincidence, the free market and the United States both value gold the same at the moment.

At this point it is well to compare gold with silver. Silver is in far greater demand industrially than is gold. Silver performs many tasks for which there is virtually no substitute, especially in the field of photography. The demand for silver is very solidly based, and can only increase rapidly. Silver prices cannot be fixed and held because we vitally need silver, and in such quantities that it must be allowed to be produced in a free market. Gold is not nearly in such a strong position; to some extent the demand for gold is one which is rooted in Man's instincts (or sentiments, or both), and it might be that this instinct could be lost, or modified, although I doubt it.

It is true, of course, that as labor and materials' costs go up the price of gold must eventually rise, or ultimately no more gold would be mined. Sooner or later the price of gold must go up, but I would feel better about investing in gold if there were a strong industrial demand to bolster the situation. Gold prices, of course, go up if a particular currency is devalued (that is, the price of gold goes up in terms of numbers of dollars, or pounds, or whatever currency might be involved), but this in a sense is not a true price rise. Prices of gold mine stocks tend to firm up also during deflation, as long as the Government will buy gold at $35 an ounce. But deflation seems to be occurring less often recently than in the past, perhaps because we have found that inflation is politically more popular and socially more acceptable.

What is gold worth, and going to be worth? The debate goes on, and it is a problem worthy indeed of the judgment of Solomon. Investing in shares of gold mines may be as much pure speculation as investment. When politics are involved, my geological training does me little good. One thing I confidently predict, however—with the present state of international economics and politics, investing in gold will prove exciting. Ask your broker for advice on how it might possibly be profitable too—and then make up your own mind. Good luck!

SILVER

Silver is the most useful of the precious metals. Its use in coins has, and will continue, to make news. Next to the U. S. Treasury Department, the largest user of silver in the United States has been Eastman Kodak Company which uses about 25 million ounces a year. With the reduction of silver use in coins which took place in 1965, the U. S. Treasury is declining in importance as a silver user, but the fact remains that industry alone in the United States used more than three times our current production, and silver demand is rising fast. Silver is likely to be in chronic short supply for the indefinite future.

Western North and South America has the silver.

It wasn't always this way, but most of the known Old World silver deposits were mined out long ago, and now most of the world's silver comes from the western portions of both North and South America. However, there are relatively few straight silver mines. That is, most silver is produced in connection with the mining of other metals, notably copper, lead, and zinc; but a few mines were fabulously rich in almost pure silver. At Hamilton, in White Pine County, Nevada, silver solutions came up through a shattered limestone and then hit an impermeable bed of shale, and the solutions spread laterally along the crest of a broken fold in the Earth's crust. The relatively soft shale was eventually eroded from the top of the mountain exposing masses of "horn silver"—a silver chloride which is soft and can be cut with a knife. The story goes that in the 1860's an Indian asked a prospector if he would like to see a mountain capped with silver. The prospector liked the idea, but had his doubts. But sure enough, the Indian led him to what is now called "Treasure Peak," and in a few years more than $30 million worth of silver was taken out. Cobalt, Ontario, is the place where a vein of almost solid native silver was discovered which had a length of about 100 feet and a depth of 60 feet and produced more than 650,000 ounces of silver. Slabs of very nearly pure silver were mined and one specimen was 5 feet long, weighed 1,640 pounds, and contained almost 10,000 ounces of silver.

These examples are characteristic of many silver mines. A few get rich at depth, but most of them are rich chiefly on the surface and can be quickly mined out. This has been the history of many mining camps in Nevada. About the time the railroad arrived and the town got half-way organized, the shallow silver deposits were exhausted. However, in Mexico one mine has been producing silver almost continuously since the time of the Spaniards, and a few mines elsewhere have had a long and distinguished producing history.

But again, much if not most silver is produced as a by-product of other mining operations. South America, which once had tremendous silver mines eagerly sought after by the *Conquistadores,* now produces only about 15% of the world's silver, and about half of this comes from the copper ores at Cerro de Pasco in Peru, a mining camp high in the Andes which I visited once. This place, by the way, is worth going to see if for no other reason than the spectacular train ride it takes to get you there. The train leaves Lima (virtually at sea level) at 7 in the morning and at 11 that same morning you cross Ticlio Pass, 16,200 feet above sea level. It is quite a trip, and well worth the 4 or 5 dollars it costs —one of the biggest train ride bargains in the world.

Present silver production by country is approximately as follows:

Country	Percent of world production
Mexico	20
United States	16
Canada	13
U. S. S. R.	10 (estimate)
Peru	10
Australia	7
Others	24
	————
	100%

Silver in strong demand.

The demand for silver can only increase, and supplies are going to be tight. It is doubtful if the price can be controlled effectively by any Government regulation, for silver must be available for industrial use, and the price must rise so that it can be mined profitably and provided to industry.

It is interesting to note, in this connection, how what one would regard as good information can be dismally wrong. In 1960, a U. S. Government bulletin had the following statement:

> "World outlook is for continuation of the rising trend in both production and consumption of silver. Notwithstanding that total world consumption currently exceeds production, large stocks are available to meet anticipated demand and no shortage of silver is expected at least in the near future. Output from domestic mines plus imports and secondary production should be ample for all normal domestic requirements."

By 1963, a research institute was awarded a government contract to study alternatives to silver in coins, because of a shortage of silver, and by 1964 the U. S. Treasury Department was openly discussing the need for replacing silver by some other metal in order to meet silver demands. Furthermore, the U. S. Treasury stockpile fell by 364 million ounces in 1964, and the Government raised its maximum share in underwriting exploration costs for new silver deposits from 50% up to 75%. In 1965, President Johnson signed into law a bill which allowed the Treasury Department to reduce or remove the silver from U. S. coins.

Here we have the principle well illustrated which is stated in the introduction to this book: chemists can frequently substitute one material for another but they have to use something—they can't make something out of nothing. Also, there is the principle that for some materials in certain uses, there are virtually no acceptable substitutes, and such is the case of silver in photographic processes and in certain other industrial uses (electrical industry, for example). Demand for silver can only go up.

Investing in silver.

Much exploration work will go into trying to meet the demand of the world for more and more silver in the years to come. You need not worry about the market—the problem will be to develop supplies. There are not many silver mines as such, but there are a few and the largest in the United States are the Sunshine Mine and the combined operations of Hecla Mining Company although even here much silver comes mixed with other metals. Canada has a number of silver mines, a listing of which is not practical here as their circumstances change with regard to prospects rather rapidly. You should check with your broker for current information. Investing in silver via the route of buying shares in large companies which produce silver as a by-product of other mining operations, is another logical approach. These companies include Cerro de Pasco, Kennecott, Anaconda, and Bunker Hill.

Occasionally, small silver mines can be found which are good investments. I owned stock in a small silver mine for many years. It proved profitable. (I paid 22 cents a share and ultimately sold it for 41 cents, and it paid some good divi-

dends at times.) It was a well managed company, whose officials were conscientious about reducing overhead. I knew
a couple of the men and they were competent and honest.
But without such firsthand knowledge, these investments are
usually a gamble. Investigate carefully, by all means.

I might add that most brokerage houses are totally un-
prepared to make considered judgments on small mining
companies. Most reliable firms know this and will tell you
so, and advise you to go elsewhere. "Elsewhere" usually
means to a mining stock broker in one of the regional over-
the-counter markets, and this can sometimes be a jungle. It
is well to proceed carefully. Gradually, however, the Securities and Exchange Commission with the cooperation of many
brokers, and particularly through standards set up and en-
forced by the National Association of Securities Dealers
(NASD) have improved the over-the-counter markets for the
benefit of the small investor. For one thing, the spread between the "bid" and "ask" price has been narrowed to more
reasonable limits.

As procedures become more orderly on these smaller
mining exchanges, the small investor has a better chance to
make money on his stock purchases. Some spectacularly good
buys have existed in the past, some probably exist right now,
and some will undoubtedly occur in the future.

The famous Sunshine Mine.

Some real silver bonanzas have been hit, and the story
of the Sunshine Mine, in northern Idaho, is an example.
Organized in 1921, and initially financed largely by apple
growers in the Yakima, Washington, area, stock was sold at
10 cents a share. It remained around that figure until the

late 20's when a few good ore stringers were found, and the
stock price went up to about $3 a share in 1929. In the de-
pression about 1930 to 1932, the price fell to 70 cents a
share. Gradually it worked up after that to the year 1936
when excellent ore was hit and the price went to $25 a share.
Since then the price has varied considerably; currently the
stock is selling in the $30 to $40 range. The Sunshine Mine
has been the largest single silver producing mine in the
United States every year since 1928,[1] and its production total
has been greater than the amount of silver taken from all
the mines in the entire Comstock Lode in all its history.

The story of the Sunshine Mine makes fascinating reading. That story told over and over again has sold vast quantities of both good and poor "penny stock" ever since. But
the fact is the Sunshine was a "penny stock" that proved to
be a terrific investment. (Lucky Friday in the same mining
district proved to be an even better investment—see its
story in the chapter on INVESTING IN MINES.)

Some personal experience.

In connection with the Sunshine Mining Company situation, I can add a bit of personal experience to show what
anyone can do. Several properties adjacent to the Sunshine
Mine apparently had good ore in them, as shown by maps
made by various geologists, and widely and freely distributed
in rough sketch form by many brokers in the Spokane area.
But reaching this ore was an expensive matter as sinking

---

[1] Hecla Mining, by its merger with Lucky Friday, and through
its other mines, is now the leading U. S. silver producing
company.

a deep shaft and equipping it costs a lot of money. So the properties adjacent to the Sunshine Mine proper lay dormant. However, as the Sunshine Mine had less and less good ore, the Company began to look at adjacent claims and finally worked out an agreement whereby some of these would be developed by using a well-equipped Sunshine shaft and then moving laterally at depth into the adjacent silver deposits. Anticipating this situation slightly, I looked at the maps, picked out a company which had special appeal on the basis just described, and bought a few shares of "penny stock." In a couple of years it increased in price very nicely, as Sunshine did enter into a development agreement with this company. I don't think my being able to make this profitable move was due to my geological background, for the maps were available to anyone, the ore vein system was well known, and sketches appeared in brokerage literature. It was just a matter of recognizing the situation and then having patience to see time work it out.

These are small situations, to be sure, but most of us are small investors, and these opportunities are big enough for our dollar resources.

Summary.

Silver is a very useful metal, and demand is increasing rapidly. Supplies of silver are currently tight, and the situation is not likely to change very greatly in the foreseeable future. It is probable that the price of silver will rise rather substantially over the next few years. Silver is produced largely as a by-product from other mining operations; a few mines producing chiefly silver do exist. Numerous small silver mines also exist, and money can undoubtedly be made in some of these situations but they should be investigated very carefully.

THE PLATINUM-GROUP METALS

Metals of the so-called platinum-group are platinum, palladium, iridium, osmium, rhodium, and ruthenium. Of these, platinum is the most abundant and important. Except for palladium, all these metals are much higher priced than gold; currently platinum is about $150 an ounce, compared with gold at $35.

From the viewpoint of the average person, however, these metals do not constitute an avenue for investment by themselves, and I include a brief discussion of them here chiefly for the sake of completeness.

These metals come mainly from placer deposits (sand and gravel deposits), or are recovered as a by-product from nickel and copper ores. There are only a few ore-minerals of platinum-group metals as such, and not in significant quantities as far as is now known. If you invest in most any of the large nickel or copper mining companies you are investing in platinum to a minor extent. For example, International Nickel Company has platinum-bearing ores which average about 3% combined nickel and copper, and about 0.03 ounce per ton of platinum-group metals.

Characteristics of the platinum-group metals include their resistance to chemical corrosion (platinum crucibles are used in many chemistry laboratories), high resistance to heat and oxidation, excellent electrical conductivity, and their ability to act as catalysts in certain processes—notably oil refining. Catalysts are materials which aid in a chemical change but which do not enter into it, and therefore are not used up.

Demand for the platinum-group metals is modest, and the growth trend is slow. Except for palladium (60% of which goes into electrical contacts), the fact that the platinum-group metals are not used up in many of their applications (catalysts, crucibles) reduces the need for replacement.

The U. S. Bureau of Mines estimates that at least 40% of the world's platinum reserves are in Africa, with the Soviet Union and Canada having most of the remainder.

Summary.

Platinum-group metals are valuable, but not to the average investor as an outlet for investment funds. Buying a stock such as International Nickel is about the closest one can come to investing in the platinum-group.

GEMSTONES AND RELATED MATERIALS

What is a gemstone is somewhat a matter of opinion. Gem materials have three principal qualities—they are durable, they have some degree of rarity, and they are beautiful. Diamonds qualify; so does petrified wood. Most gemstones are used for decorative purposes; diamonds come in two forms—gem diamonds and industrial diamonds. Most diamonds are the latter kind and as diamond is by far the hardest substance known, its use in cutting tools is important (diamond drills for core-hole work in mining, diamond saws for cutting precious and semi-precious stones, et cetera).

Most men at some time in their lives invest in gems—at least one gem, the diamond. Tradition has it that you give a diamond to your lady of choice, and the diamond producers and marketers of South Africa are busy perpetuating the idea, as are lots of young ladies.

Aside from this sort of investment in gems, the average investor does not find many opportunities to put his money profitably in these things. The United States is markedly lacking in deposits of precious gemstones, although common gemstones are abundant, and this field we will explore a bit.

At this point, a few basic facts might be in order.

The term "gemstone" is applied to uncut materials. The term "gem" applies only to cut stones. Gemstones are divided into precious and semiprecious stones. The difference to some extent is value, but also the precious stones are among the harder stones, including the diamond, the hardest of all materials. Precious stones commonly include the diamond, emerald, ruby, sapphire, and sometimes fire opal is included, although strictly speaking it does not belong. Of these stones, the diamond is the most popular; the emerald is the most valuable, weight for weight.

The semiprecious or common gemstones include amethyst (a purple variety of quartz found chiefly in Brazil and India), beryl, garnet, jade, peridot, quartz, spinel, topaz, tourmaline, turquoise, zircon, and a whole host of materials which are silica (SiO_2) just as is quartz, but unlike quartz are non-crystalline or only very finely crystalline. These include the "thunderegg" of Oregon fame (the official State rock), petrified wood, and an almost infinite variety of agates (moss agate, ruin agate, sagenite agate, iris agate, and so forth). If your community has an annual rock and mineral show by all means visit it. You will be amazed to see what beautiful things have been found virtually in your own backyard.

Actually, what is a gemstone is largely a matter of taste. More than 100 materials have been so classed. But again, how does the average person invest in such things beyond making a simple personal purchase? The opportunities for investment are not great, but they do exist. Nearly every person at one time or another picks up a pretty rock or mineral and thereby becomes a "rockhound." There are at least several million people who pursue the hobby more or less regularly. It is a good hobby—one in which all the family can participate, and it is inexpensive.

"Rockhound country."

Until recently, no one was particularly concerned about "rockhounds" and their children ("pebble pups") invading public lands and collecting rocks; but this has proved to be such a rapidly rising tide that now some regulations are in effect as to how much can be taken out in any one year. Many good deposits occur on private lands, also, and here is where some investment potential may exist. In Oregon, where I have lived for a number of years, ranchers in the eastern and central parts of the State sometimes open their lands to "rockhounds" for a small fee, and make a modest amount of money this way. The "Priday agate beds" north of Redmond, Oregon, have operated this way for years, for "thundereggs" are abundant there. Fossils, I should add, are much the same situation. If the deposit is unusual and showy, sometimes the specimens can be sold, or exhibits developed which will be a public attraction. Some areas have tremendous quantities of petrified wood. A bulldozer cutting through a hill to put in a new ranch road may turn up a new deposit at any time. I am inclined to believe that "rockhounds" will be with us for a long time, and opening areas for these people to work in at a reasonable fee is a logical development, which is already being done in places. Naturally, like everyone else, I would prefer to collect where the collecting is free, but I have also paid small fees to go into certain private areas and always felt I was getting my money's worth.

There are many special situations which have been developed in this regard. A good example is the case of the fossils in the famous dinosaur track quarry near South Hadley, Massachusetts. Here, dinosaurs ran across mud flats 200 million years ago during the Triassic Period, and left their tracks now preserved in stone. These have been quarried for a long time and sold as interesting conversation pieces to be put in the stone wall of your den, in your fireplace mantel, or on your patio. The dinosaur track market is not quoted in most papers, but last I saw, a good track was going for about $12 to $15. Iron ore is sold by the ton—dinosaur tracks are sold by the foot. (With apologies to the reader.) The man who operates the place seems to have done reasonably well. In addition to selling tracks, he has some nice displays, issues you a "dinosaur hunting license" (limit *"Brontosarus*—1 only, not less than 10,000 pounds live weight. *Giganteum*—1 only, legal length 60 feet"), and has a situation with considerable merit both as a commercial venture and as an educational exhibit.

Other such situations exist or have existed. I once knew a man in Kemmerer, Wyoming, who for years quarried fossil fish from the 60-million-year-old lake beds a few miles west of Kemmerer near the now-defunct town of Fossil (still a railroad place name). I have one of these fossil fishes, and whereas it cost me $3 at the time, I would not now take $50 for it. Whether this deposit could be worked again commercially, I don't know—the man eventually ran into severe overburden problems; but at one time the quarry did produce some of the best preserved fossil fish in the world, and specimens were shipped to all parts of the globe, both to museums and to private collectors. I think a fine roadside exhibit could be developed there. The specimens were certainly worth looking at and would make an excellent and educational tourist attraction.

Diamonds.

Diamonds being the most popular precious stone, a word about them is worthwhile. Most diamonds come from Africa where De Beers Consolidated Mines Limited controls over 80% of the world diamond output. This firm not only produces gems but also synthetic diamond grit (for abrasives). To invest in diamonds essentially means investing in De Beers, and some of its shares, "American Shares," are traded in the U. S. over-the-counter market.

Probably you have also noted that cut diamonds are advertised in our newspapers as investments. I wrote for the literature about this, and I can neither confirm nor deny the claims made, but it was stated that over the past 20 years $1000 invested in a home would now be worth $2700, in industrial stocks $4800, in a farm $3200, and in a diamond $3000.

Diamonds in Arkansas.

The United States does have one area where diamonds have been found—in Pike County, Arkansas. This area is privately owned with a high fence around it, and tourists are allowed (indeed, encouraged) to dig—for a fee. To lend an air of excitement and authenticity to this situation, it used to be (and perhaps still is) the rule that you had to sign a card stating that any diamonds above a certain size which you discovered as you prospected the area you had to share with the owner of the mine. Otherwise, whatever you found in the way of smaller diamonds were all yours. Diamonds do definitely occur there, but with all the tourist traffic, I think it is a fair statement to say the place has been well picked over.

Undiscovered North American diamond deposit?

An interesting sidelight on the general lack of any diamond mines in North America, is that there is apparently one diamond deposit waiting to be discovered somewhere in eastern Canada. In the sand and gravel deposits brought down from that area by the glacier, diamonds have been found in West Virginia, Ohio, and Wisconsin. The original source is unknown but it has to be somewhere north of these localities. Copper nuggets were found in glacial deposits in Finland and traced back to their source, and by this procedure one of the better copper mines of Europe was discovered. Perhaps one day Canada will be a diamond-producer. Might be an interesting summer vacation project

—combine diamond deposit hunting with a Canadian fishing trip. You could hardly lose on that venture.

Synthetic gems.

Diamonds are now made synthetically by General Electric, by De Beers, and by a Swedish firm; but these do not seem to be of gem size or quality; at least, they don't seem to have invaded that market so far. Rubies can also be made synthetically, and I understand the way to tell artificial stones from natural rubies is that the natural specimens have flaws in them which the artificial stones cannot quite duplicate. Also, a man in California has developed a process for making synthetic emeralds. He didn't patent the process because he feared non-patent agreement nations such as Russia and Red China would steal the process, which apparently is a good one. He makes emeralds which the jewelers for a long time could not believe weren't real. I have seen some of these synthetic emeralds and compared them with the real thing and they are very similar indeed. This process still seems to be one man's secret.

Summary.

Investing in gems, gemstones, and "rockhound" type materials is a limited field. However, local special situations occur, and some investment opportunities, especially along "rockhound" lines, do exist, or are discovered from time to time. Perhaps some of the ideas and examples just presented will stimulate your imagination to see possibilities in the region where you live.

Non-Metals

"Metals" and "non-metals" is a basic classification of our mineral resources. In common usage, non-metals do not include coal, oil, or natural gas (although they are non-metals, of course); these are so large and important in our economy as to be usually considered individually. But a host of very useful materials do come under the heading of "non-metals." These include gypsum for the wallboards in your house, sand for the glass in your windows and television set, and salt for your morning plate of bacon and eggs. In dollar volume, non-metals far outbulk the metals. Gold mines are great, but the fact is that gravel pits are even greater, dollar-wise, in annual production. Non-metals are a very large field for investment, and on the following pages are described some of the more rapidly growing phases of this group of natural resources, places where investment capital is needed and can be profitably employed. Other materials are also mentioned which, although perhaps not growing any faster than our economy as a whole, are nonetheless in a very solid position and constitute not only a fairly profitable outlet for investment capital, but also a hedge against inflation—one of the chief investment attractions of natural resources.

CEMENT

The Romans made cement 2,000 years ago, and some of it was so good that structures built with it are still standing (the Roman Forum, the Appian Way, the Aqueduct). There are various kinds of cement; the type most commonly used today being portland cement, named from the Island of Portland off the coast of England where a very good limestone occurs which is used as a building stone. The man who invented cement (Joseph Aspdin, in 1824) named his product after the fine building stone to try to aid in its acceptance as a building material, too.

When we say that someone invented cement we indicate that it is not strictly a natural product, but there actually are some natural cements. Although portland cement is man-made, it is a rather simple mixture of some elementary raw materials. Portland cement is chiefly a mixture of limestone and clay, made by grinding and blending the materials, burning them in a kiln to form a clinker, grinding the clinker back to a powder (sometimes a little gypsum is added at this stage), and finally putting it in the standard 94 pound sack. Cement is not to be confused with concrete, which is the product obtained by mixing cement with water, sand and/or gravel and possibly other materials (pumice, asbestos, et cetera).

U. S. is largest factor.

The United States is both the largest producer and consumer of cement in the world, accounting for about one-fifth of the total. Current production is more than 360 million barrels. Development of a domestic cement industry is imperative for any country which has industrial plans at all; cement is heavy and it cannot be shipped far conveniently. In addition, materials for making cement are so widespread that it is not necessary to ship cement to very many places except the markedly undeveloped areas. The United States does export a little cement but this amounts to less than 2% of total production.

A big business.

In dollar volume, the cement business is one of the largest segments of the mineral industry (more than $1 billion a year). About a dozen or so companies in the United States account for more than half of the cement production; but there are over 100 companies, great and small, in the business. In times past, the demand for cement has commonly exceeded predictions, but occasionally the cement industry seems to have decided to do something about this situation, and temporary over-production has been a problem (this was recently the case).

Investing in cement.

From the point of view of the small investor it is generally not feasible to try to invest in land which contains the
raw materials for cement manufacture. There are just too
many such sources, although exceptions occur. In the very
rapidly growing Willamette Valley of western Oregon there
is no known source of good raw material for cement manufacture. If one had such a deposit, I feel confident a cement
manufacturer could be induced to buy it and build a plant.
Certain other localities also do not have cement plants as
close as might be desired, and cement must be shipped in
from some distance.

However, for the average investor, investing in cement
manufacturing companies is the logical avenue of placing
funds. As already indicated, there are many such companies
but the majority are small. Cement manufacturing is a low-
margin, high-volume situation, which is relatively stable (or
as stable as the general level of the construction industry on
which it depends). From time to time, however, because of
expanded local construction needs (a big new military installation, for example), well situated smaller cement plants
have yielded excellent profits, and generally speaking the
cement business has been reasonably profitable. It is not a
spectacular performer, but it is a basic industry not likely
to go out of style, and it is growing. One cement plant operator, Martin Marietta Corporation, states that by 1980 America's cement needs will double to 750 million barrels a year.
The cement industry, however, is somewhat less a hedge
against inflation as compared, for example, with oil, gas,
silver, or copper. As the cost of the raw material is relatively

small, the chief costs of cement are manufacturing costs (labor, fuel, and capital outlay for machinery).

Almost as important as a source of limestone and clay for cement making, is a convenient and cheap source of fuel for heating the rotary kilns wherein the cement is burned. Low cost fuel and an abundance of limestone is the combination which produces cement, and one reason why cement companies have gotten their starts best in Pennsylvania, Ohio, Illinois, and Texas—states where limestone, clay, coal, oil, and natural gas are in abundance. Successful cement operations include not only these raw materials but also a good local market. With the great growth of Eastern cities early in our history, all these factors combined to make the Lehigh Valley of Pennsylvania the largest cement-producing area in the United States many years ago, a position it continues to hold.

Almost every brokerage firm will have an already prepared list of cement manufacturers for you, with statistics on sales, earnings, and profits, and probably some recommendations. As construction activity varies from one part of the country to another, the relative attractiveness of various cement companies for investment will likewise differ at any given time, so it is important to have current information.

Summary.

Cement is big business, it is a relatively steady business, and the long term trend of consumption is up. The raw materials are a small part of the cost of operation, so it is less of a hedge against inflation than are other types of natural resource processing companies; but the business is basic, and as an income investment with moderate long term growth, cement is a good place to put funds. Local building booms (especially freeways) can provide better than average returns for certain strategically located cement plants. The shifting pattern of construction makes it important that you obtain good current information from your broker.

SAND AND GRAVEL

Would you rather have a gold mine or a gravel pit? I suppose there is more glamour to owning a gold mine, and who would decline a good one? But good gold mines are rare. Good gravel pits are not. Furthermore, the price of gold, at least in the United States, is controlled by the Government. Labor and material costs go up but the price of gold does not, and gold mines are being forced out of business by this squeeze. But sand and gravel pits are opening up every day and there is money to be made in such common materials.

Location is important.

You can't afford to ship gravel very far—location is a prime concern. With the construction of more and more freeways and other building projects, need for new local gravel sources is continual. This circumstance presents investment opportunities. With all the new construction planned—especially highways—the need for sand and gravel will continue to be enormous.

How do you invest in sand and gravel?

To begin with, it is a fairly simple business in which to invest. You aren't involved in any complicated chemical processes, demand is fairly steady for a well located gravel pit, your inventory can't be stolen very easily, and it is a reasonably predictable business. If there seems to be a demand, or you anticipate at some near future time a demand for gravel and sand, you might go talk with your state geological survey about local sources. They usually have studies made on these resources and can suggest a close supply which you can purchase or lease, perhaps. Commonly the state geological survey will have a bulletin on the topic, covering the state county by county.

If an area is the site of considerable construction, and gravel and sand are being hauled in from some distance, this is a circumstance worth investigating to see if you can find a closer source. You may turn up nothing at all, but if you do find a closer source, the matter of hauling costs will soon make the contractors come beating a path to your door—or gravel pit. If you already own land, you might determine what sand and gravel is on it, and talk with local contractors to see if your deposits of these materials are commercial.

In general, buying stock in sand and gravel operations involves buying into local situations on a relatively personal contact basis. However, a few of the larger companies are traded over-the-counter nationally, American Aggregates Corporation being an example. Your banker might have some suggestions as to local people who would welcome your participation in a project, or simply talk to some of the larger contractors. Remember that a lot more dollars' worth of gravel are produced each year in the United States than dollars' worth of gold.

BUILDING STONE

Early Man lived in a natural stone house called a cave. Then he moved out of the cave, presumably to something better. But the low maintenance costs of the cave (didn't need to be painted), and the fact that rock is a good insulator against heat and cold appealed to him. So now he has rebuilt his rock house around him by cutting stone and using it for constructing homes and office buildings. Stone is durable. It costs very little to keep up. It has many things in its favor as a building material.

By "building stone" we mean, more properly, "dimension stone"—stone cut to a size or broken to a more or less uniform size, rather than crushed stone which is used in driveways, as an aggregate in concrete, et cetera. Slate we usually include as a building stone.

You might think the matter of building stone was a simple situation—stone is stone. But there is an almost infinite variety of building stones, each with its own characteristic pattern, color, texture, and many other distinctive qualities. With the great variety of architectural styles coming off the drawing boards, and the many types of building stones, the possible combinations are very numerous, and many of them exceedingly attractive.

Stone, of course, is an item markedly subject to freight costs when it comes to competing with other building materials. But this is the factor which will allow the small investor to profitably develop local building stone sources. As a geologist, I have frequently been asked by local contractors as to where they might obtain supplies of interesting and attractive building stones. I find in checking sources of building stones used locally here in western Oregon that some come from as far away as Tennessee, Minnesota, and Indiana. For special trim on buildings, dimension stones from New England, Minnesota, Indiana, and even Italy go to nearly every state in the Union.

Demand for local stone.

But the closer to home good building stone can be found, the more likely it is that the stone will be used in a given area. Good building stone is in demand almost everywhere, and if you can find a supply, you can market it in at least small amounts rather readily. Local contractors will often provide men to quarry the stone, if necessary, and it can be a small operation—almost a one-man venture. This sort of thing is not going to yield any handsome profits, but if you have a good building stone quarry on one corner of your 160 acres, it can pay the taxes on the place and perhaps a bit more.

What constitutes good building stone.

Good building stone should be attractive to the eye, and relatively easy to work (break). It should be durable so that later exposure to air and water will not weather it excessively, and it should not have impurities in it such as clay lumps or iron-bearing minerals which will leave streaks on the rock after a time. In the quarry, the rock should not show too many joints (all rocks are jointed, but some are so minutely jointed as to not make suitable dimension stone, whereas other stone has joints so spaced that they will actually be an aid to quarrying).

Investing in stone companies.

Use of stone in buildings seems to be enjoying a good growth rate. For example, a small company in southern Minnesota, Delano Granite, Inc., has for the past several years had an annual growth rate of 20%. However, as each stone quarry produces a rock which, in effect, is different from any other rock, each case merits careful consideration. But basic demand for building stone seems to be strong, although for architectural popularity reasons, one stone (and therefore one stone company) may do much better than another.

Some large stone quarry companies do exist, notably in Indiana, Minnesota, Tennessee, Vermont, New York, and Georgia. Some of these are privately owned, or locally owned by investors. Some are more publicly held companies. Indiana Limestone Company is one such publicly held firm. Your broker can tell you about others.

Slate.

Slate is almost too specialized a situation to merit more than brief discussion here, but it is included to round out our consideration of building stones. Slate's chief use for a long time has been in roofing, but the very quality which makes slate so famous tends to commercially defeat slate—

its great durability, along with the factor of weight. A slate roof will outlast several buildings underneath it, and slate roofs have been transferred from one building to another as the building below fell apart. But slate is so heavy that part of the advantage of little or no maintenance costs is lost in the extra cost of building a supporting structure strong enough to hold up a slate roof. Slate roofs may last 500 to 1,000 years or more, but there isn't much demand for that kind of durability.

More recently, slate is increasingly being used in hall-way entrances, and in various types of trim, and not so much as roofing material (although crushed slate is used as roof rock sometimes). However, use of slate has not expanded proportionately with the building industry, for it has had to meet severe competition from other more easily handled and less costly materials. Slate has survived as a roofing material, particles of it being mixed in asphalt shingles to give them durability. Also, slate is used as an aggregate in cement blocks.

Most slate in the United States comes from the north-eastern states, with minor amounts from North Carolina, Georgia, Arkansas, and California. Slate is not a very profit-able item at present. As a rock in crushed form it has lots of competition, and gets no benefit from its unique character-istic—that it can be split into sheets. This, of course, is what made it a natural roofing material, but there has been no way discovered to cheaply do this by machine. It is largely a hand operation and has been so for hundreds of years. Labor costs are high.

For roofs with a 1,000-year guarantee, slate is fine, but as an outlet for natural resource development capital, it is not so attractive.

Summary.

Building stone is in increasing demand. Because of the weight of the material, freight is an important consideration, and local sources of good stone adjacent to any moderately-sized city will be valuable. Building stones come in an almost infinite variety, and certain distinctive and attractive types may possibly even find a nation-wide market. Stock can be purchased in stone companies chiefly in local over-the-counter markets. Although growth is not likely to be spectacular, some companies have shown as much as a 20% annual increase in business over a number of years.

CRUSHED STONE

Crushed stone has a wide market. Logging companies use it to surface their roads; state and county highway departments use vast quantities of it. Home owners use it for their driveways, in their patios, and in many other ways. It is used in making concrete and for chemical purposes. Some gravel companies are also in the crushed stone (or rock) business, for gravel is a convenient item to crush. The prospects are for the crushed stone business to expand along with industrial activity, and the future looks good.

In choosing stone for crushing—if you have a choice—one characteristic which is desirable is that it be less hard than the machine which is trying to crush it. I was once a consultant to a situation where the rock-crusher was trying to crush rock (it was granite) which was substantially harder than the rock-crusher and it was the rock-crusher which was being crushed more often than not. We eventually found a limestone deposit several miles away which proved to be a very happy solution to the problem, as limestone is considerably less hard than steel and for this reason, among others, about three-fourths of crushed stone is limestone. Granite makes a pretty sort of crushed rock—varicolored, but it is hard on the rock-crusher, and is more expensive for that reason.

Crushed stone, except for certain special types shipped in for use on roofs, on stucco walls, et cetera, is like sand and gravel—very much a local situation. You can't afford to ship it very far. Ways to invest in crushed stone are similar, in general, to how you would invest in building stone, or in sand, and gravel, which has been described.

CLAY

We sell and use about 50 million tons of various kinds of clays in the United States each year, which figures out to be about a quarter of a ton per person. Clay involves large quantities of material but not too much money in general, for the 50 million tons were valued at only about $175 to $200 million, or about $4 a ton. Nevertheless, the uses of clay are many, varied and fundamental (bricks, pottery, tile, cosmetics, electrical porcelain, in rubber, et cetera). The largest single consumer of fairly high grade clay is the paper industry which uses these clays as filler and as a coater.

Varieties of clay.

There are many kinds of clay. The U. S. Bureau of Mines recognizes six principal categories:

Kaolin: (Also called china clay, and other names). Used for china, in rubber, paper, refractories, et cetera.

Ball clay: (So-named because of its plasticity). Used for china and ceramics in general, and fillers.

Fire clay: Used for refractories (brick linings in blast furnaces, for example), for crocks, jugs, jars.

Bentonite: A weathered volcanic ash, chiefly. Two types exist—a swelling type and a non-swelling type. Some swelling types increase from 15 to 20 times over their dry volumes. Used in making special muds for oil well drilling and in foundry (casting) sands.

Fuller's earth: Used as absorbents and as cleaning agents.

Miscellaneous clays: Includes brick, sewer pipe, and common tile clay.

Clays are heavy, and freight enters into the economic picture, just as in the case of common salt which cannot be shipped very far without running into competition from other deposits elsewhere. However, there is only one kind of common salt, and there are many different clays for special uses. At least one case exists where clay from as far away as Georgia was shipped to a California manufacturer—until a California deposit of the same sort of clay was found. Here is an approach to getting into the clay business: find a closer source and cut the freight costs.

Clay-products companies.

There are numerous clay-products companies ranging from those which make common brick and sewer tile to those that make refractory products (North American Refractories, Glen-Gery Shale Brick Corporation, Harbison-Walker Refractories, Ferro Corporation, and many others), to those which make ceramic tile (for example, Stylon Corporation), pottery, china, and porcelain. Some are listed on the national stock exchanges, some on regional exchanges; some are strictly local investor enterprises. In general, in buying stock in clay processing companies you also buy clay deposits, as most companies have their own supplies.

Clays, of course, are common, and none is really significantly in short supply. Clay for common brick is in virtually unlimited quantity.

However, if you want to pursue the matter of developing new clay deposits, or think you have such a deposit on land you now own, go consult with your state geological survey, or write and ask them for a list of publications on clays in your state. Also, they may be able to help you in other ways. The pamphlet listing all the publications of the Kansas Geological Survey includes this statement:

> "Clay and shale samples are tested, and information will be furnished on ceramic raw materials in the State. A file of 2,000 samples of ceramic raw materials is maintained for ready reference by members of the industry and other interested people."

If you are interested, go talk with your state geological survey.

Keep in mind, when considering the economics of clay deposits—as well as other sorts of mineral deposits—that these benefit tax-wise in the United States from a depletion allowance. The Internal Revenue Service can give you exact figures on any particular item. On clay it currently ranges from 25% for certain specialty clays to 5% on ordinary brick and tile clay.

GLASS

Why do certain materials, even rock materials, let light through them whereas others do not? Nobody seems to know the answer for certain; among other things we are still arguing about what light is. Natural glass which will transmit light occurs in many places—we have lots of it in the lava flows of central Oregon. Man has improved on this material a bit for his own purposes. Glass has been found in the ruins of civilizations which date back to 4000 B.C.

Light goes through glass, and is absorbed by materials in a room which then give out energy but in a form which will not travel back through glass, and thus your house can be heated by the Sun—greenhouses are. Besides transmitting light, glass has a variety of other interesting properties, and glass manufacturers have been exceedingly energetic and ingenious in finding new uses for glass. I am sure they have not reached the end of the road on this matter by any means. The increased amount of glass used in today's buildings as compared with 30 years ago is striking; compare an old picture of a city with a recent one. The old city was built of concrete, and brick; the new city is built of aluminum, steel, and glass. Engineering work on space heating, utilizing the "greenhouse effect," has given glassmaking a further impetus.

Glass, through much research on it, has now become a cheap and good construction material, and its use has been increasing at the expense of other materials. It will probably continue to make such gains and show a better than average industrial growth rate.

Companies such as Libbey-Owens-Ford, Pittsburgh Plate Glass, the Corning Glass Works, Mississippi Glass, Anchor Hocking Glass and a number of others are in a very interesting business, and one which seems to offer both solid growth along with the possibility of some truly striking technological break-throughs.

Glass is made from quartz sand, with a variety of other things added in minor quantities to give it special properties. In the Midwest, a nearly pure (99%) quartz sandstone called the St. Peter Sandstone provides an excellent source for glass sand. In New York and Pennsylvania, other good glass sands exist. Elsewhere, the raw material supply is not quite so favorable, but the raw materials for making glass are abundant so there is no urgency to find more. Investors can invest in glass best by buying shares in glass manufacturing companies. Perhaps we are getting a little far from a natural resource when we talk about manufactured glass, but glass, as we have noted, does occur in nature, and man-made glass can be perhaps regarded as only a short step from nature's product—nature had the idea first. The situation is analogous to cement or bricks. There is one company which apparently does specialize in producing silica (the material from which glass is made), the Pennsylvania Glass Sand Corporation.

But buying into glass companies involves buying the raw materials too, as most firms have their own sources of raw material. Glass is an important item in our economy, and its use is rapidly increasing. Glass is a solid growth industry with the possibility of some spectacular new applications being developed.

ASBESTOS

Asbestos is both one of the most unusual minerals we have, and one of the most useful. It is unusual because of its physical appearance—it is fibrous, and some of it consists of fibers up to 6 inches long which look more like silk than mineral material. Crysotile is a long fiber form, and more than 6 miles of thread can be spun from one pound. Certain types of asbestos can stand temperatures up to 5,000 degrees Fahrenheit.

To fully list the uses of asbestos would fill many pages, but principally it goes into brake linings, all sorts of fireproof cloth, insulating materials, shingles, and wallboards.

Canada has largest deposits.

The largest known asbestos deposits in the world, by far, are in Quebec in an area about 6 miles wide and 70 miles long (a small part of this trend extends into Vermont). Less than 10 companies produce most of the asbestos from this region (commonly called the Thetford area, named for a town). Other deposits do exist in Canada, however, in Ontario, British Columbia, and in the Yukon. The Soviet Union has important deposits, and a number of deposits are known and worked in Africa.

California now in substantial production.

Until recently, the United States produced relatively little asbestos with small deposits known in Vermont, North Carolina, Georgia, Montana, Arizona, and California. Although not to be compared with the Canadian deposits, California in 1959 experienced a modest "asbestos rush" in Fresno and San Benito counties. Deposits were found and mills built. Johns-Manville, the Atlas Minerals Division of Atlas Corporation, and Union Carbide Nuclear Company (a division of Union Carbide Corporation) are among the active firms. Also, in 1959, Jefferson Lake Sulphur Company (now owned by Occidental Petroleum Corporation) core-drilled a long-known but poorly explored area in Calavaras County, California, and proved up more than 20 million tons of rock (the total deposits in the area are much bigger) containing $6\frac{1}{2}\%$ asbestos of the short fiber grades (long fiber is the more valuable). This apparently is a commercial deposit, however, as a company was formed (Jefferson Lake Asbestos Company) and a mill built which can process up to 2,500 tons of rock per day.

More recently, U. S. Asbestos Company began operating a plant in this same area (there are about 4 plants now), and a company spokesman for that firm said that the 700 acres which they hold contain reserves of 25 million tons of asbestos-bearing rock with a fiber content which ranges between 15 and 20 percent. Estimated capacity of this plant is 25,000 tons of fiber a year.

Mills now operating in California have an annual capacity in excess of 75,000 tons of fiber per year. (This compares with something over 1 million tons of Canadian production.) Still other asbestos deposits may await discovery in the United States, as suggested by the following personal experience.

Undiscovered deposit?

I taught for several years in the College of Mines at the University of Idaho. Forestry students there were required to take General Geology. Many of these men were excellent students, and I became well acquainted with a number of them. One fall, a student from the previous spring class came into my office with a specimen of some of the nicest long fiber asbestos I have ever seen. He had been hired as a smoke-jumper (a fellow who bails out of airplanes over remote regions in a parachute to fight isolated forest fires) in one of our Western states that summer, and had jumped to put out a fire in a particularly wild spot. He told me that he had landed on the very edge of the fire and had to quickly get out of his chute harness and run down the hill to get away from the blaze. As he ran, he noticed the hillside was strewn with specimens of the sort he brought in to show me, and he had picked up this single specimen. A stiff wind was blowing, and he had to go quite a distance to get out of fire danger and decide where and how best to fight the fire. He was busy for the next several days fighting the fire and finally had to walk out several miles.

He showed me on a map roughly where he had been, but he was not quite sure himself on which drainage line he had found the asbestos sample. I marked the general area on a map, but it is in such a remote spot that I am not likely to get to it for a long time. Nevertheless, it gives me a certain feeling of excitement like the urge the old prospectors must have had, to think that somewhere there perhaps is a good deposit of asbestos waiting to be discovered. Maybe one of you will find it while you are on a pack-trip vacation through our Western mountain areas. Keep your eyes open for a silky-looking mineral. Of course, the crux of the matter is the size of the deposit; asbestos has to be a big volume operation to pay, but there apparently was a lot of material strewn on the surface if it was noticed by someone fleeing from a forest fire, and the quality of the specimen I saw was good. The deposit would have to be core-drilled to determine its quality and extent for sure—but who knows?

Wide range of grades.

Asbestos in quantity, however, as far as is known today, is mostly in eastern Canada. But even here there are different grades, and some companies seem to have better deposits than others. Annual report comparisons will sometimes give you a clue as to which company is having few problems with asbestos quality and which are working with less desirable materials.

Asbestos as an investment.

Asbestos is not likely to be a spectacular price performer as far as shares in companies are concerned, but this sort of investment will provide a steady income (and the investment certainly should be bomb-proof!). It is probably also a good hedge against inflation as asbestos is used in so many ways in our economy that there will always be a demand for it. Asbestos occurs in relatively narrow veins or seams in rocks;

the volume of rock waste is enormous and causes disposal problems. Efficiency of operation is of prime importance. There being no general shortage of asbestos, it is a matter of improving milling operations and profit margins through technology. The company doing this best will make the most money.

Johns-Manville Corporation, Asbestos Corporation, Ltd., and United Asbestos are among companies having properties in eastern Canada. Cassiar Asbestos Corporation has been developing properties in western Canada, and currently is opening up new production in the Yukon Territory near Dawson.

SALT

There are many kinds of salts, but when we say "salt" we almost always mean common salt, sodium chloride—NaCl. It is one of our most useful materials. We cannot live without it (yet it is interesting to know that it is made out of two violently poisonous elements, sodium, and chlorine). You can preserve fish with it, gargle your sore throat with it, and use it in thousands of chemical processes, as well as on your ham and eggs.

Investing in this indispensable material is frustrating because it is so common. A great sea once occupied parts of New Mexico, Texas, Oklahoma, and Kansas (during Permian time, about 250 million years ago), and left behind, over an area of more than 100,000 square miles, salt deposits with an average thickness of 200 feet.

You might guess offhand that a substantial part of the

salt used in the United States would come from such a logical source as the Great Salt Lake in western Utah, where it
can be had by the millions of tons merely for the shoveling.
But this is not so. Salt is found in great quantities not only
in Salt Lake, and in the southwest, but also as buried deposits
in Michigan and New York, and in tremendous domes of
salt which have punched their way up through the soft sediments of the Gulf Coast region. I was once down inside a
salt mine in one of these domes in the swamps of Louisiana,
600 feet below sea level, and I never was or will be in a drier
spot. The salt had been squeezed up, or probably flowed up
under the influence of a gravity differential (the salt was
lighter than the adjacent sediments) and great taffy candy-
like patterns in the banded salt were visible in the walls and
roof of the mine, a striking sight.

When considering investment in a single salt mine, or
in a firm which is only a salt-mining company (and not a
salt-chemical producer), the factor of freight rates should be
kept uppermost in mind. Freight costs to major markets
chiefly determine the value of salt at any given location, for
salt is sold on a "delivered" basis. Investing in salt as just
salt, is probably not a particularly outstanding place to put
money for rapid appreciation of capital. Salt is exceedingly
common; the U. S. Bureau of Mines estimates that the
United States' known salt reserves are sufficient for more
than 100,000 years even assuming a consumption rate 100
times greater than at present.

Salt-chemical companies.

Salt is a basic material for a variety of important chemicals. Companies which both mine and process the salt into

these chemicals have done very well, and are likely to continue to do well. Two excellent examples are International Salt Company which has paid a dividend every year since 1915, and Pennsalt Chemicals Corporation which has paid a dividend every year since 1863! Both are listed on the New York Stock Exchange.

SULFUR [1]

Sulfur has a wide variety of uses, and demand is going up very sharply at the present time. In fact, during 1965 the Free World used 1,100,000 tons more than we produced! Production went up but demand went up faster. In the United States, demand was up 9% in 1965 over 1964. Demand continues to rise sharply, chiefly because of the increased need for fertilizer to help feed hungry millions. Sulfur is a prime ingredient in the production of certain types of fertilizers, this use now accounting for about 40% of all the sulfur used. Demand is not likely to be any less in the future—quite the contrary. It is significant that farmers in western Europe and Japan, for example, apply as much as 450 pounds of plant nutrient per acre while the U. S. rate is about 40 pounds an acre. Rising land and labor costs insure that farmers will be forced to try to make each acre of land they now have produce more, and fertilizer is their principal tool in this regard.

---

[1] "Sulfur" is now the preferred spelling, but some corporate names still retain the older spelling of "sulphur" because of legal problems involved in changing.

Besides fertilizer, sulfur is involved in a variety of other products to the extent that if any one industry is on the bottom of its economic cycle and not using much sulfur, some other industry is likely to be in the reverse position. This very wide industrial use imparts a stability to sulfur demand which many other raw material producers can envy. Furthermore, new uses are being found for sulfur.

Where do we get sulfur?

Sulfur is obtained from native (pure) sulfur deposits (in the United States chiefly in the cap-rock of salt domes in the Gulf Coast), from smelting of iron pyrites and other sulfide ores, from natural gas, from petroleum, and from coal. The United States produces most of the world's sulfur; Mexico is second. The bulk of U. S. production is by a relatively few companies, chiefly from salt domes where it is obtained by the Frasch process, a method whereby hot water pumped down a pipe into the sulfur deposit melts the sulfur and this hot water and sulfur is then pumped out through another pipe.

There was a modest sulfur shortage during the period of 1950-1953, but increased exploration solved the problem, so for a time there was a sulfur surplus. But now demand is rising, and in 1965 the Free World produced 22.5 million tons and consumed about 23.6 million tons, drawing on stockpiles for the difference. Accordingly, any company locating new sulfur deposits will have little problem in marketing the material. Companies such as certain oil and mining concerns which obtain large quantities of sulfur as a by-product of their regular operations, have a definite plus-factor going for them.

For example, Pan American Petroleum Corporation (wholly owned subsidiary of the Standard Oil Company of Indiana, and not the same company as Pan American Sulphur) has a number of sulfur-producing plants in connection with oil fields both in Canada and the United States, as do many other companies, large and small. Husky Oil Company has a small plant (about 30 tons of sulfur per day) in Wyoming.

Sulfur occurs to some extent (up to $5\frac{1}{2}\%$ by weight) in almost all crude oils and also in natural gas. This sulfur was previously regarded as undesirable, but now efficient processes have been devised for removing it from oil and gas. In general, it has to be removed anyway, whether the sulfur is sold or not. Being able now to sell sulfur at increasingly better prices, means that companies with "sour" crude oil and "sour" gas (sour = sulfur content of more than $\frac{1}{2}$ of 1 per cent) can now make an asset out of a liability.

Also, there are large quantities of sulfur locked in low-grade metal deposits (pyrite, common "fool's gold"—is a compound of iron and sulfur). Invention of a new process to economically produce these deposits both for their metal and their sulfur would, in effect, be a way of "discovering" new sulfur reserves. Some sulfur is recovered from this sort of source now. (Sulfur from smelter fumes.)

Major sulfur-producing companies include Freeport Sulphur Company (No. 1 U. S. producer), Texas Gulf Sulphur Company (No. 2), Gulf Sulphur, Pan American Sulphur, and Jefferson Lake Sulphur Company (a subsidiary of Occidental Petroleum Corporation). And, as noted, many oil companies produce sulfur as part of their oil operations. Most brokerage firms have at least one man in their research department who follows sulfur stocks rather closely, chiefly because of the recent strong demand for sulfur, the accompanying rise in price of the stocks of the companies concerned, and attendant rise in investor interest. These brokers can give you current information and recommendations. The scene changes fairly fast; recently several oil companies were successful bidders on Gulf Coast offshore acreage wherein sulfur deposits may be expected, and the results of subsequent drilling may move these companies into the select circle of major sulfur producers. *The Wall Street Journal* will undoubtedly keep up on these developments.

Sulfur is in a basically strong long term growth situation. The problem is generally more one of finding new supplies to keep up with demand, rather than any marketing difficulties.

LIME

Lime is the second largest tonnage chemical in the United States. It was used as a plaster and mortar in Egyptian pyramids 4,000 years ago, and it has more than 7,000 modern uses.

Lime is very reactive to water and never found alone in nature. Chemically it is calcium oxide or calcium magnesium oxide and it occurs as part of limestones and dolomites —very common rocks. Ohio, Missouri, and Pennsylvania are the three principal lime-producing states, and supply about one-half of the Nation's needs.

Lime has a tremendous variety of uses. It is important in steel manufacturing, petroleum and sugar refining, in water treatment, in making paper and bleaching powders, in plasters and cement, in soil neutralization and conditioning, and in many chemical processes. It is so broadly interlaced with our economy that the use of lime tends to follow rather closely the general trend of industrial activity and growth. Lime is in a strong position in that it has chemical properties not duplicated readily by other materials, and further, it is so cheap that it almost always eliminates competition on this basis.

Lime plants depend on high quality limestone and dolomite deposits. However, in general, lands with lime resources would not be an outlet for investment for most investors— there are too many possible sources and the raw material cost is low. Processing is the major cost of lime products. To invest, one would invest in companies in this business. Currently there are about 150 lime plants in the United States, owned by many companies, both large and small. A number of large companies, with diversified operations, have lime-producing divisions (for example, U. S. Gypsum, Kaiser Aluminum and Chemical), and there is a host of small lime companies throughout the country, some traded on local over-the-counter markets. Again, your broker can turn up names of companies in most any area of the country you might be interested in. Lime companies are in a steady basic business which will probably show no unusual growth trends but should definitely grow as fast as the economy as a whole.

GYPSUM

The United States is both the world's largest producer and consumer of gypsum. Gypsum is used in plaster, as a soil conditioner, in dry wall-board construction, and in hundreds of other ways. Gypsum mining is currently conducted in about 30 states, but in spite of this there are areas where gypsum must be imported for some distance—into the Pacific Northwest, for example. But gypsum reserves are not a problem. The U. S. Bureau of Mines estimates we have sufficient supplies now in sight to last at least 2,000 years.

Gypsum, historically, has offered a solid sort of investment, if the dividend record of the leading company, U. S. Gypsum, which dates back without interruption to 1919, is any indication. Standard and Poor's Corporation (investment statistics and advice) also gives the common stock of U. S. Gypsum an "A—" rating which is unusually good for a common stock. Other gypsum companies (and there are many) include National Gypsum and Bestwall Gypsum (now merged with Georgia-Pacific Corporation).

Growth of the gypsum industry can be expected to occur at least as fast as the economy as a whole, but its heavy reliance on the building field may cause some fluctuations. To invest in gypsum, buy into companies with their own mines; most large and many small companies manufacturing gypsum products do have their own sources.

BORAX AND BORON

Borax is a boron compound. It and elemental boron are being used in rapidly increasing amounts both in the United States and abroad. Production is expected to *at least double* the next ten years. The range of products and processes using boron and borax is extensive. They are used in soap and cleansers, glassmaking, steel alloys, and in many other ways including such interesting and possibly spectacular areas as the space program and in the field of atomic energy. Most borax and boron is produced from deposits in California where reserves are regarded as ample for at least 100 years.

Transportation is a problem as borax is bulky, and whereas the United States' boron minerals are located in the far West, the markets are principally in the manufacturing areas of the East and Midwest. However, because other sources are limited and also relatively remote, the matter of freight has not been a fatal problem to boron mineral use. Almost half of the United States' production of boron minerals is exported. Turkey is the second largest boron mineral producer in the world, but is currently far behind the United States. However, Turkey's reserves appear to be quite extensive, and may be more of a factor in world markets in the future than at present.

Extensive research programs by both the Federal Government and private industry have found and continue to find new uses for boron and boron compounds. The outlook for the industry is good. Domestically, four companies dominate the production of boron minerals. These are, in order of importance, U. S. Borax and Chemical Corporation ("Death Valley Days"), American Potash and Chemical Corporation, Stauffer Chemical Company, and Kern County Land Company. Callery Chemical Company, although not a factor in mineral production, has done a good deal of work with boron as a fuel.

POTASH

The term "potash" is loosely applied to a variety of compounds of potassium—an element which is fundamental to all life. Potash occurs in nature in a number of ways, but chiefly in the form of salt deposits remaining from isolated arms of the sea which once spread across continents, including North America. Some salt lakes such as Searles Lake in California and the Great Salt Lake also contain potassium compounds.

Potash is used in many industrial processes including soap-making, synthetic rubber manufacturing, and glass making; but in the United States 95% of the potash is used in the production of fertilizers. Potassium is absolutely essential for plant growth, and the practice of cropping lands and removing the crop to other areas instead of letting the annual crop rot back down into the ground as it would do naturally, means that lands are continually having their valuable elements removed, of which two important ones are potassium and phosphorus (see section on PHOSPHATE). Fortunately, however, the known world reserves of potash are sufficient for many hundreds, if not thousands, of years at present or even accelerated rates of consumption.

The search for new potash sources, therefore, is not particularly urgent, and probably would not be a profitable sort of enterprise, especially for the small investor. Furthermore, the geology of these deposits is such as to suggest that we probably have found most of the big deposits, at least in North America, where we have perforated the Earth's crust with drill holes as has been done to no similar degree in any other part of the world. The world over, Russia seems to have the largest deposits, with East Germany second, West Germany third, Canada fourth, with Spain and the United States tied for fifth place. But even in fifth place, the United States has tremendous reserves, located chiefly in New Mexico. Most of these lands are owned by the State or Federal Government and are leased to firms for potash mining operations.

In Canada, tremendous deposits are located in Saskatchewan. These are now being developed by several companies, including Noranda Mines, Ltd., which is spending about $73 million on a 62,000-acre property, about 40 miles east of Saskatoon. Here, some 800 million tons of material averaging 30% potassium oxide have been proved up by drilling.

The problem with potash is not supply of basic raw material. Many companies hold big reserves. The problem also is not demand in the sense that demand may come and go. The demand is here and increasing rather steadily. But the abundance of potash and the obvious fact of its importance have led a great many companies, both here and abroad, to go into the business. Eastern United States can be supplied cheaply from deposits in Germany. Canadian potash can readily move down across the plains and into the northern Midwest. Competition is severe, but efficient producers will no doubt make money.

Investing in potash.

Investors can participate in potash resource development through shares of the many companies which operate in this field. U. S. Borax, Homestake Mining, and Swift and Company jointly are opening mines and a plant with an annual capacity of more than 1 million tons in Saskatchewan. Other potash producers include American Potash and Chemical Corporation, International Minerals and Chemical Corporation, (Lithium Corporation is just going into the business), and a number of others. Your broker can supply you with an up-to-date list of companies. With competition so severe (and indications are it will continue that way), the slight advantage one firm may have over others in freight costs, quality of deposits, mining methods, or a variety of other factors, will be important because profit margins are small. Some of these circumstances can shift fairly rapidly, so it is necessary to get current information in order to invest wisely. But with potash you have the assurance of investing in a very essential and definitely growing industry, dealing with a material which is vitally important to every living thing.

PHOSPHATE

The world has lots of problems. Keeping phosphorus in circulation is one of them. Perhaps you never thought about it, but there is only so much phosphorus in the world and it has the unfortunate habit of getting locked into rocks of various kinds. But all vertebrates, including Man, must have phosphorus. Indeed, all animals and plants seem to require some phosphorus. Keeping it in circulation is most important, and International Minerals and Chemicals Corporation, FMC Corporation, American Cyanamid Company, Monsanto Company, W. R. Grace and Company, Occidental Petroleum Corporation, and about 30 other companies are continually working on the problem. Believe me, they are in a basic business as our populations expand.

Phosphorus compounds are used in a variety of ways, but about 70% of all phosphate rock produced in the United States is used as fertilizer, a use of phosphate by Man which dates back at least to 200 B.C. This percentage is likely to increase, and the total amount of phosphate used will surely increase rapidly as soils around the world become less fertile, and each acre of land must be farmed more intensively as food demand, labor costs, and land prices all go up.

The United States has the largest phosphate reserves in the western hemisphere, and second largest in the world. Phosphate occurs in more than 20 states but the 3 principal areas are in Florida, Tennessee, and in the Western mountain region of Montana, Wyoming, Utah, and Idaho.

I have done geological work in this "Western Phosphate Field," as it is called, and the phosphate rock reserves there are impressive, with reports indicating as much as 3 billion tons. I used to collect fossils from some of the phosphate beds, and one time published a report on some of them. The most interesting one I found (we found 18 of these unusual fossils all together) was part of a shark—a jaw which grew in a spiral shape. This toothy spiral fossil has been found also in Russia and Australia. It stirs my imagination to think of the seaways which once connected these widely separated areas, and of this shark's swimming about in western Australia, central Russia, and what is now the Northern Rockies. To this ancient sea we owe our great Western phosphate reserves, which are vitally important.

Phosphate demand growing fast.

Demand for phosphate is growing faster than the rate of growth of our Gross National Product, and seems likely to continue to do so, as intensive agricultural practices increase. If eating is basic, then phosphate will be in demand, and with world populations currently doubling every 23 years, phosphate is going to be very, very important.

Investing in phosphate.

The geology of phosphate deposits in the United States has been studied rather thoroughly. Major new discoveries are unlikely. However, reserves already known are sufficient for a great many years to come. Investing in phosphate is chiefly a matter of investing in existing companies processing phosphate, and almost all such companies have significant reserves. It should be noted, however, that the importance of the phosphate business to the various companies differs, as almost all are also engaged in other operations to a greater or lesser extent. We have already listed some of these diversified companies. However, any company well established in the phosphate business as part of its operations, has a definite plus factor in its attractiveness as a long term investment. There is absolutely no doubt but that the demand for phosphate will only go up, and more rapidly than the general rate of our economic growth.

MISCELLANEOUS NON-METALS

Agricultural lime(stone).

Much of what is termed "agricultural lime" technically is not, but simply fairly pure finely crushed limestone spread over the fields to sweeten the acid soils. We have this problem of acid soils in western Oregon where heavy rainfall leaches out the soil, and organic acids accumulate from decaying vegetation. The soils need to be periodically reconditioned, but unfortunately this is one part of the United States which does not have good limestone deposits, and lime and crushed limestone has to be hauled in from considerable distances. But, in general, agricultural limestone can be obtained close by and local needs satisfied.

Some cement companies produce agricultural limestone. It is a high volume product but with only modest profits. However, it is a steady item and, like other sorts of soil conditioners and fertilizers, agricultural limestone will undoubtedly be used more and more to keep our agricultural areas healthy and producing the vast quantities of food which we will surely need.

The agricultural lime and limestone business will probably grow as fast as the economy in general—perhaps a bit faster. It may not be a spectacular performer but it has inherent stability from serving a very basic cause—providing our food supply.

Diatomite.

Diatomite is a rock made of the accumulated shells of an interesting little plant called a diatom, which has lived and still lives in both lakes and the oceans in fantastic numbers. A single cubic inch of diatomite has been estimated to contain the skeletons of as many as 25,000,000 individual diatoms. And at such places as Lompoc, California, diatomite deposits can be measured in cubic miles!

Although a diatom is a plant, it swims around like an animal. It secretes a shell made out of silica—something like glass. The shells are hollow and of various shapes. Machines have been made which will actually sort out various shapes of diatoms, for some have special uses as filtering agents for various materials such as oil and sugar.

Diatomite is also used in hundreds of other ways including in abrasives, in paints, and in cement. The largest amount of diatomite goes for insulating and construction materials. Diatomite is about 90% space (the rock will easily float on water), it has a high melting point, and therefore is an especially good insulator against fire, sound, and temperature.

Diatomite occurs in every state of the Union, and is mined in about a dozen of them. California, Oregon, Nevada, and Washington produce most of our diatomite. There are less than a dozen companies operating diatomite plants, chief among which are Johns-Manville and Eagle-Picher. We export a small amount of high quality filter-type diatomite. The United States is self-sufficient in diatomite, and raw material sources are not a problem, although good deposits along the East Coast of the United States would be welcomed as this area is without any to date, and supplies have to be shipped in from some distance. However, geologically, the chances of finding any such deposits are not good.

Investing in diatomite, for the average investor, means buying stock in companies now in production, two of which we have named. This is hardly a field for investment in itself. Diatomite production in all cases is just a small part of a diversified company's operations. But I thought you might like to have a little background in what diatomite is when you read the annual reports of some of these firms. Johns-Manville uses the trade name "Celite" for diatomite insulating material, and Eagle-Picher Company has called

it "Celaton." In both cases these firms are selling literally
trillions of fossil plant skeletons.

Other non-metals.

The small investor may possibly encounter other non-
metals in which investment opportunities are offered him,
or he may find these materials listed as part of a group of
products which a company may sell. The following list is by
no means complete, but briefly describes a few of these materials, how they are used, and their importance.

> Feldspar: Very common mineral used in making porce-
> lain, pottery, tile, and other ceramic products. No
> shortage of raw material in the United States or
> elsewhere.

> Helium: A gas vital to some military and medical ac-
> tivities. Helium occurs in small quantities in nat-
> ural gas, chiefly in southwestern United States. No
> other country except possibly the U. S. S. R. has
> helium reserves comparable to those of the United
> States. The Government currently controls helium
> production; companies are required to sell it to the
> Government or to other customers by permission of
> the Government. Income from helium is a small
> factor for some oil companies (*e.g.,* Kerr-McGee,
> Hugoton Production).

> Mica: A plate-like or flake-like mineral used in elec-
> tronic industries and in a variety of other ways.
> Mica mining becomes almost a hand operation in
> places, although it has been mechanized to some
> extent. Demand has fluctuated considerably as the

Government has stockpiled it from time to time. Comes in many different grades. Some small mines have operated at times with only a few men, and been profitable, if a good deposit was available.

Perlite: A glassy rock with a small amount of water in it which pops like popcorn when heated. Used as a lightweight aggregate for concrete, as an insulating material, abrasive, et cetera. The United States is self-sufficient. Produced in volcanic areas of our Western states.

Pumice: Frothy lava-originated rock. Will float on water. Used as lightweight concrete aggregate, insulator, road material, et cetera. The United States has ample supplies in Western states. Use will grow with economy and closely parallel construction industry trends. Deposits can be and are developed locally by small investors, profitably.

Talc: Soft, light mineral used in paint, rubber, paper, crayons, and, of course, talcum powder, along with many other uses. The United States has ample reserves. Use will probably increase more rapidly than rate of growth of economy as whole. There are about 30 small companies in the United States that mine talc. Some have stock shares which are publicly traded. Ask your broker.

Water

Nothing, absolutely nothing, can live without water. We may live on land but our whole civilization is built on water.

Each person uses tremendous amounts.

How much water do you account for each day? Most people will merely add up what they drink, use for washing their face and hands, for taking a bath, and maybe for washing the car. In classes I have taught in which we discussed the subject, the students generally guessed from 15 to 50 gallons a day. *But the answer is probably closer to 15,000!* If you want to run around naked you can cut your water consumption; otherwise you have to figure in the fact that it takes 800,000 gallons of water to raise an acre of cotton from which to make your clothes. If you wear wool clothing the proportionate figure (for raising sheep per acre) comes out even greater. One pound of beef from a two-year-old steer represents a consumption of 2,900 gallons of water when figured from alfalfa to steer to beef. You account for about

700 gallons of water when you eat a hamburger. It takes 65,000 gallons of water to make a ton of steel, 70,000 gallons to make a ton of high quality paper, and about 64,000 gallons to produce a ton of rayon. People are busy inventing things that take more and more water, and people ardently save money so they can buy these things—automatic dishwashers, automatic washing machines, backyard swimming pools.

Water, in several ways, is big business and it will be a much bigger business soon. Consider these impressive statistics reported by a U. S. Senate Committee on National Water Resources. The committee estimates that between now and 1980, $228 billion will have to be spent developing water resources in various ways. The total present investment in water facilities in the United States is less than $200 billion.

Water—a renewable and reusable resource.

The amount of fresh water in the world is strictly limited and quite unequally distributed, but unlike oil, for example, which is used once and gone forever, water is a renewable resource. It comes new to us in every rain and snow, and it also can be reused once it is here. Water going down the Ohio River is used more than 100 times before it reaches the Mississippi. It is used for cooling processes in oil refineries and steel mills, and in doing so the river actually gets hotter as it moves along. It also becomes polluted. To make water usable again it must be processed, or treated, whichever you choose to call it. The treatment of water produces new water—at least it makes useful water out of liquid which previously could not be used.

Investing in water.

Most water supplies (lakes, rivers) are in the public domain so it is difficult to buy water. But you can invest in water processing companies (*e.g.*, Calgon Corporation, Nalco Corporation, Crane Company, Culligan, Inc.). In effect you are investing in water supplies by buying shares in these firms, for they make equipment and chemicals and provide services which result in unusable water's becoming useful water again. And you can invest in water companies—companies which distribute water, and there are about 3,500 investor-owned utilities, most of them small. Here is a partial list of some of the larger ones which are traded more or less regularly in the over-the-counter market: American Water Works (this listed NYSE), Bridgeport Hydraulic, California Water Service, California Water and Telephone, Citizens and Utilities, Elizabethtown Water, Florida Water and Utilities, General Waterworks, Hackensack Water Company, Indiana Gas and Water, Jamaica Water Supply Company, Ohio Water Service, Pennsylvania Gas and Water, Philadelphia Suburban Water, San Jose Water Works, Southern California Water, Southern Gas and Water, Southern Gulf Utilities, and Utilities and Industries. These are utilities, of course, and like utilities the price performance is usually not spectacular; but the dividend records in many cases have a long and distinguished history of making payments and growing steadily. Note that many of these also offer other services besides water (gas, telephone) so you are buying into water in varying degrees depending on the company.

Water permeates many investments.

When you invest in a great variety of things you are also investing in water to some extent. When we talk of investing in water we get into a situation where it is hard to determine where your investing in water really stops and where you are investing in something else. Many industrial operations need large amounts of water for their plants and have developed water supplies to meet these needs. So when you buy into these companies you are also buying into water supplies. Ample water supply is something which nourishes many investments, in effect, and I am serious when I say that one should consider the matter of water with almost every investment. For example, we have already pointed out that one of the critical factors in the development of the Colorado Plateau oil shales is the matter of water supply.

Let me approach it another way to illustrate. At one time I calculated how much water there was available behind each share of national bank stock in two different states—both fairly rapidly growing areas. I took the state geological survey's figures on how much fresh water there was available for daily use, and divided that by the number of shares of bank stock. I think that there may be some correlation (other things being equal) between how fast an area grows and how good its water supply is. Banks depend on population expansion for their growth, and I think that "well watered" bank stock, in this case, is the thing to buy.

You also buy into water when you buy real estate. In this regard I will freely admit that I think Florida has a great future; indeed it is now our fastest growing state. People move toward the Sun, especially in their old age. Water and sunshine are a magic growth mixture, and Florida has it. The Kiplinger News Service thinks so highly of the area that it publishes a special *Kiplinger Florida Letter*. I think they have something there. When you invest in Florida you are investing in both water and sunshine—a hard combination to beat. Ponce de Leon may not have found the Fountain of Youth, but if he had bought Silver Springs, Florida, from the Indians at any reasonable price (say about the amount paid for Manhattan Island), he would have had a fountain of gold.

Processing fresh water—a strongly growing investment area.

But to return to a more nearly direct approach to investing in water, keep in mind that the supply of fresh water is strictly limited. Our existing supplies must be used—not once but many, many times, before the water is finally allowed to reach the ocean. For the long term, desalinization of salt water has a large investment potential, and this field is growing now, but a presently stronger growth trend, I believe, is in the area of treatment of fresh water.

One reason I believe this is the better place for investors to put their money for more immediate results is the fact that we are now "piped in" to these existing fresh water supplies. The great industrial users of water such as the steel mills, the oil refineries, the chemical plants, as well as our cities, are not going to move. They are going to stay where they are and depend on existing water supplies which are becoming increasingly polluted, and by the same token will need an increasing amount of water treatment. To support this view I quote a man who ought to know, Frank

DiLuzio, head of the Interior Department's Office of Saline Water. He states, "Desalinization isn't the answer to this country's water problems. It may be in some arid Near East countries where water is so desperately needed. . . . But in this country it's often cheaper to pipe in fresh water, or process polluted water."

Another problem of using sea water for any large water supply situation is what to do with the salt. New York City uses about 1 billion gallons of water a day. If this were taken from the sea, there would be a residue of 120,000 tons of salt per day! What do you do with that?

At least 50 million people in the United States today drink "second-hand" water—water which has already been used by someone else in some fashion. Many people drink fourth or even fifth-hand water. Processing water so it can be used again is big business and it is going to get bigger. One Government official estimates that the total water clean-up job cost in the United States will come to 50 billion dollars. In November, 1965, the State of New York voters approved a 1.7 billion dollar "clean water" bond issue.

The U. S. Department of the Interior estimates U. S. water consumption in 1965 at 359,000 million million gallons a day, and predicts a 600,000 million million gallon daily use by 1980—*nearly double in just 15 years.* There is only so much fresh water in circulation at any one time. We are going to have to re-use it more and more before finally allowing it to go back to the sea, eventually to be returned to us again by nature's own water purifying and distribution system—evaporation, transport in clouds, and then coming to earth as rain and snow. Companies which either partly or wholly derive their incomes from water treatment in some fashion such as Calgon, FMC Corporation, Nalco, Culligan, Crane Company, American Radiator and Standard Sanitary Corporation ("American-Standard") and several other firms stand to benefit handsomely from these circumstances.

Desalinization of sea water—a long-term growth field.

At least 60 nations at present have water shortages; the nations of the Middle East are especially concerned. They have lots of oil but little fresh water, and, as they have said many times, "we can't drink the oil." So they are selling their oil and buying other things, and as the population grows, they are likely to be using more and more of their oil revenues for buying water de-salting equipment. We are concerned with the problem in this country, also— thus the recent creation of the Office of Saline Water, which has already been mentioned.

Various methods can be used to de-salt water. Some involve distillation, some use the principle of osmosis, some use freezing, and there are other techniques. Distillation is one of the more common of these processes. Companies which have something to offer in the way of water de-salting techniques include Nalco Chemical, Westinghouse, General Electric, Foster Wheeler Corporation, American Machine and Foundry, Aqua Chem, FMC Corporation, Koppers Company, Carrier Corporation, Aerojet-General, and Ionics, Incorporated. Recently, D. C. Burnham, president of Westinghouse, told stockholders that Westinghouse was prepared to build and guarantee a plant which could convert 50 million gallons of sea water daily—enough to supply the personal needs of a city of 500,000 persons. This plant would use either nuclear or ordinary fuel. Westinghouse now has on its order books or has built plants to convert salt water to fresh water at more than 30 localities around the world. The company built the plant which supplies the U. S. Naval Base at Guantanamo, Cuba, after Castro cut off the water supply.

A General Electric official recently stated: "There's a profitable multi-million dollar market in desalinization in the years to come."

Summary.

The water treatment industry is justly viewed as a great growth business. Short term trends favor companies concerned with fresh water treatment. Longer term investments can logically be placed in de-salting processes. Your broker is quite likely to have recent reports from his firm's research department on this topic, with investment recommendations. Ask him.

Air

You don't have to drill or prospect for air. It's here but what do you do with all this vast resource? Air Reduction Company has some ideas; as does Air Products and Chemicals, Union Carbide Corporation, and a number of other companies.

Air has a simple composition.

An "ocean of air" is the expression sometimes heard, but the atmosphere and the oceans are different in, among other things, the fact that almost every element in the Earth is to be found in the ocean whereas air has a relatively simple composition: Nitrogen 78%, Oxygen 21%, Argon 1%. This adds up to 100% but the figures are rounded off, and there is enough space in the decimal points for traces of carbon dioxide, neon, helium, and several other gases, in very small quantities. The possibilities for air chemistry, therefore, are perhaps not so great as in the case of ocean chemistry.

Also, the growth possibilities for strictly air chemistry

seem rather limited. Oxygen, for example, can be obtained in a variety of other ways besides from air; the same is true of nitrogen. So air has competition, and the rate of growth of air chemistry companies seems to be steady but moderate. However, all of the companies involved in air chemistry are becoming more or less diversified general chemical companies working with a variety of raw materials. As such, Air Reduction, for example, has had an excellent growth rate recently.

Air as a source of energy.

Air can also be a source of energy—in the form of wind. This energy has been utilized for many years, in a minor way, especially on the Great Plains, in the form of wind-powered electric generators. At the moment, developments in this direction seem limited, but perhaps some invention—a high tower or set of towers in the right place (could we ever figure out a way to harness a jet stream?), with the right highly efficient equipment, might make the wind a significant source of power, and a place for investment capital.

Air purification—potentially a large field.

To directly invest in air, chemical companies dealing with air-derived products may be the closest approach. However, one can also consider investing in air in terms of investing in devices which will process air to make it clean—that is, to treat polluted air just as we now treat polluted water.[1] Actually, we are doing this to some extent already, and we will be doing a lot more of it soon. In 1963, Congress passed the Clean Air Act, and subsequently provided millions of dollars for research on this problem, and well they might. A former health commissioner of New York State says: "Millions of citizens are living in an ocean of air that is, on good evidence, unhealthy to breathe." A considerably stronger statement comes from Dr. Morris Neiburger, professor of meteorology at the University of California (Los Angeles), who says he doubts we can control air pollution and that eventually, possibly within the next hundred years, "All civilization will pass away, not from a sudden cataclysm like a nuclear war, but from gradual suffocation from its own wastes."

Air pollution is a problem just beginning to get serious consideration in many areas. Almost everywhere, however, action is far less than it should be on the matter, but this will simply *have* to change. A staff report to the Committee on Public Works of the United States Senate, 89th Congress, 1963, entitled "A study of pollution—air" contains the estimate that air pollution in the United States, in effect, costs $65 per person per year, adding "This could represent an annual cost to the Nation of over $11 billion." Obviously, prevention and control of air pollution is already very important economically, and the base for a large industry is here right now.

No major companies currently appear to derive sub-

---

[1] There is this difference, however, between air and water pollution treatment. Water can be treated either before it returns to natural water bodies, or as it is taken out of rivers and lakes for use. Air, however, can be effectively treated only when it returns to the atmosphere. Once pollutants get into the general atmosphere, it is not practical to try to remove them by any man-devised system. It is up to nature.

stantial income from this situation. A few smaller companies are relatively more involved, one being American Air Filters Company (listed NYSE); another is Commercial Filters Corporation (over-the-counter). Ask your brokerage firm's research department about the field of air treatment. Investment opportunities are going to come; some should be appearing now. Incidentally, Dr. Neiburger points out that such things as fuel cells might be the answer to air pollution, if used in place of gasoline-burning engines. Perhaps this is one reason why oil companies are pushing research on fuel cells. (See chapter on FUEL CELLS). Between the fact that fuel cells are much more efficient than are internal combustion engines, and the fact they do not pollute the air, they may possibly be the happy answer to two basic problems—the increasing costs of liquid fuels, and our air contamination difficulties which are due in large part to the burning of liquid fuels.

Summary.

Investing in air as such may be a relatively limited field, but investing in devices involved in cleaning polluted air [2] may rather rapidly become a sizable outlet for investment capital. Laws already on the books concerning the use of anti-smog devices on cars provide the basis for a growing anti-air pollution industry.

---

[2] American Radiator and Standard Sanitary Corporation has recently been running ads in popular magazines calling attention to their electrostatic precipitators which remove ". . . over 99% of the solids from smoke before it leaves the stack. One American-Standard precipitator, recently installed, is compact and inexpensive, yet can remove a hundred tons of fly ash a day."

The Oceans—Last Great Frontier on this Earth

The oceans cover 71% of the Earth's surface, and constitute the last great physical frontier on this planet. In 1963, a special oceanographic research committee of the National Academy of Sciences—National Research Council stated that ". . . there exist no accurate charts of over 95% of the ocean."

One of the fastest growing research fields is oceanography, and rightly so, in my opinion, for we are likely to find a lot more useful things for Man's needs the next hundred years or more by exploring our oceans than by flinging very expensive hardware into outer space, and to the Moon and Mars.

Invest in the ocean?

"Wealth from the sea?" was the title of a recent article in *Barron's*. Can you invest in the ocean? Yes, it can be done today. Dow Chemical Corporation started in Midland,

Michigan, extracting magnesium from brines of deep wells there—water trapped in sandstones in Michigan when these sands were deposited in a sea that covered Michigan some 300 million years ago. But as demand for magnesium grew, Dow Chemical had to find a larger source. The company finally discovered a process whereby it could commercially obtain magnesium from ordinary sea water, and does so now at plants on both the East and Gulf coasts. At the present time, most of the U. S. magnesium production comes from sea water, as well as does 80% of its bromine supply. Research is underway by several companies on problems related to extracting other materials from the ocean.

The oceans—a chemical storehouse.

The oceans contain about 3.5% salt by weight, of which 77% is common salt. Theoretically, all elements are found in sea water; the problem is to concentrate them economically. Although the percentages are small in many cases, the actual amount of material when stated in terms of quantity per cubic mile of sea water is very large, and the figure is even more impressive when it is realized that the oceans contain some 300 million cubic miles of sea water.

We know where these resources are. It is a case of technology's discovering economical ways to produce them. *At current prices, each cubic mile of sea water contains $6 billion worth of minerals!*

The challenge is great, and here again I would hazard the guess, as in the case of mining ventures in low grade ore, that it will be the bigger companies with strong research staffs which will make the break-throughs. How to find

MINERALS PER CUBIC MILE OF SEA WATER (APPROXIMATE)
IN TONS

Sodium chloride (common salt)	120,000,000
Magnesium chloride	18,000,000
Magnesium sulphate	8,000,000
Calcium sulphate	6,000,000
Potassium sulphate	4,000,000
Calcium carbonate	550,000
Magnesium bromide	350,000
Bromine	300,000
Strontium	60,000
Boron	21,000
Fluorine	6,400
Lithium	470
Barium	235
Iodine	235
Copper, manganese, zinc, lead (not counting manganese nodules on sea floor)	90
Uranium	7
Silver	1.4

out what is going on along these lines? There is no easy way to do it—you can check annual reports of companies likely to be interested in this sort of thing for references to what research they are doing, or read the papers carefully for the occasional news item. *The Wall Street Journal* and *Barron's* are especially good at keeping up on this sort of thing. A small news item may give you a clue to bigger things and allow you to buy in on the ocean floor, so to speak.

Several years ago the press reported an ocean survey party found a vast area of the South Pacific sea floor covered with manganese nodules. This seemed to go unnoticed for a time and then a company was formed to look into the possibility of dredging these up. It seems to me this line of endeavor has considerable possibilities, for it is estimated that there are 1.5 trillion tons of these nodules on the sea floor. Especially interesting is the fact that they are still forming today at rates faster than our current consumption of the metals involved. These nodules contain not only manganese, but also nickel, copper, and cobalt. For example, nickel is forming 10 times as fast in these nodules as our current consumption rate of this metal. This sort of mine has real possibilities—where the ore is forming faster than you need it!

We are prospecting the oceans now.

Prospecting in the ocean has already started. The U. S. Bureau of Mines, in conjunction with Lockheed Aircraft and International Minerals and Chemicals, have constructed a ship which will explore the Pacific continental shelf for manganese, phosphorite, and a variety of other materials. The Union Oil Company has obtained a lease on 30,000 acres of phosphorite nodules off the coast of Southern California. Shell Oil Company is going to mine gold in now-submerged beaches off Nome, Alaska. It has been known for years that sea level during glacial time was several hundred feet lower than it is now—the ice locked up water on the land in the form of glaciers, sea level fell, and beaches were formed then which are now submerged as some of the ice has melted. They mined the gold on the beach at Nome for years, but why didn't they think of the fact there were older beaches extending out beneath the sea?

Now this idea is apparent and the new gold rush is on. Diamonds are being recovered from at least 12 different submerged fields off the African coast. Iron is being mined in the ocean near Japan, and tin is mined in waters off Malaya.

We know less about the ocean floor than we know about the surface of the Moon! Here is a great frontier for exploration and investment. (Write for a free copy of "Oceanography, The 10 Years Ahead" from the Interagency Oceanography Committee, Building 159E, Navy Yard Annex, Washington, D. C. 20390.)

Mines on the ocean floor?

There are some good geological reasons beyond the scope of this book why the continents rather than the ocean basins are likely to be places where ore deposits will be formed, especially the richer deposits. Nevertheless, there is the distinct possibility, even the probability, that the rocks of the ocean floor (not just the nodules forming on the surface) may have tremendous potential for mining. From time to time newspaper writers (in the Sunday supplement, for example) picture rocketships going to the Moon and Mars to load up on iron ore, copper, and other such materials for transport back to the Earth. The economics of this situation as well as other factors, in my opinion, place this prospect in the far distant future. It may never be feasible. I am aware that they laughed at Columbus, but I will stand on my statement. The ocean basins are much more logical exploration objectives, and it wouldn't surprise me to hear that some mining company has staked a set of claims on the ocean floor and opened a submarine mine. The problems of submarine mining will be severe, but a lot less severe than in going to the Moon for our metals.

Farming the ocean.

The ocean is being farmed right now, at least locally. Oyster beds are an example of this. Seaweed is harvested off the coasts of Japan and sold for food. Sooner or later it may be that the oceans will be planted, cultivated, and harvested just as land is today. Although parts (especially the deeper parts) of the ocean are a virtual desert as far as life is concerned, it has been estimated that *almost 90% of the total vegetation of the world is produced in the oceans.* This is due to the fact that the area of the oceans is very much greater than that of land (71% versus 29%), and also because land has just one surface on which to grow plants whereas vegetation in the ocean involves not a surface, but a zone 600 feet or more in thickness (representing the depth to which light will effectively penetrate). Life does extend to great depths in the oceans but it all ultimately has to depend on the small floating plants, which in turn have to live where there is light. The continental shelves are by definition those areas which are covered by less than 600 feet of water (although this geologically is not exactly correct). These shelves include millions of square miles. North America has some broad continental shelves—particularly off the East and Gulf coasts. Eventually these areas may be farmed, and possibly farmed extensively. Already research has been conducted on this matter, and the term "ocean agriculture" is being heard.

As land is devoured by residential areas—one day it is an orange grove, the next day it is a shopping center, a freeway, or a new suburb—Man will have to turn more and more to the sea. Other countries such as Japan and Norway have felt this pressure for years. We have to stretch our imagination a bit, but not too much, to visualize a firm called "Continental Shelf Farms, Inc." selling stock and opening a new era for farming and investment. Or could you imagine a company named, for example, Seaplant Corporation, getting profitable things from seaweed? You don't have to use much imagination, for Seaplant Corporation exists at New Bedford, Massachusetts. Seaweed right now yields economical amounts of gels used in ice cream and other products. In Scotland, the seaweed business is now about a $4 million a year enterprise.

Energy from the ocean.

The subject of tidal energy is discussed in the next chapter, but two other possibilities for deriving energy from the ocean should be mentioned. One of these has been studied extensively and some equipment already invented to test it. The results are good enough to suggest further research is justified. This is the idea that energy can be derived from the fact that the deeper ocean waters in places are much cooler than are the surface waters (true in the tropics). Using this temperature differential, energy can be produced in various ways. Also, the ocean has tremendous currents in it. The Gulf Stream has been calculated to have an energy of 75 million tons a second. Conceivably, devices could be made which could be installed in such a way as to utilize part of this energy. (It should be mentioned at this point, however, that tampering with oceanic circulation might involve markedly changing the climates for some countries. England is in the latitude of Hudson Bay, and depends on the Gulf

Stream for a moderate climate. Without the Gulf Stream, all my Scandinavian ancestors would have had to have been Eskimos.)

Summary.

The ocean is already yielding minerals in commercial quantities. This field can and probably will be greatly expanded soon. The sea can also yield much more in the way of food for Man than it is currently doing; farming the sea is an idea just beginning to be explored. The oceans are a great physical frontier, and a great frontier for investment. Population pressures will force us into the oceans, and investment capital will be needed to be sure we swim rather than sink. Representing 71% of the Earth's surface, the oceans cannot much longer be ignored, and in many different ways they are now being invaded for the benefit of Man.

The Tides and the Earth's Magnetic Field

For the sake of completeness, two other natural resources—potential energy sources—should be mentioned. These are the tides and the Earth's magnetic field.

Harnessing the tides has long been a dream of Man. As early as the 12th century, residents along the Rance River in France built crude mills for grinding flour which were operated by the ebb and flow of the tide. Anyone viewing the sea for very long cannot fail to be impressed by this world-wide energy, available twice daily (or perhaps continually if you could devise the proper scheme). In some places the tides are only a foot or two; in other localities they are as much as 50 feet. Special situations where tides funnel into estuaries (drowned river valleys) like the Bay of Fundy in Nova Scotia have been the object of much study.

Until recently, it has not seemed the tides could be harnessed economically, but apparently the problem has been solved at least in one place. The French Government is now completing a tide-powered electric plant on the Rance River estuary—the world's first such installation.

Because funds expended in this area of research have had little positive assurance of being recovered, these studies have largely been Government projects. I am not sure private investors will have a chance to put money into the tides, but perhaps some private power company will come up with a workable system, or do so in partnership with the Government. The Passamaquoddy Bay project—lying between the U. S. and Canada—is now being revived.

The amount of potential energy in the tides can hardly be ignored, and you will be hearing more of this in the future, I am sure.

Earth's magnetic field.

A second force, which, like the tides is of Earth-size, is the Earth's magnetic field. It is the force which causes the compass needle to swing about and point north-south. The force exists. How can it be harnessed? So far nobody seems to have even a reasonably good idea, but the problem is intriguing, and it represents a tremendous challenge. Keep it as an "imagination stretcher." If you have any ideas on the subject, I am sure energy-concerned corporations (for example, utilities) would be interested. Perhaps someone will come up with an idea on how to harness this force, and you can invest in the Earth's magnetic field. Fifty years ago, if you had told people they could eventually invest in a satellite which orbited around the Earth and which could be used as a relay station for television programs ("what's television?") you would have been laughed off the floor of the New York Stock Exchange, where right now Comsat (Communications Satellite Corporation) stock is setting new price highs.

Imagination, the Earth's resources, and investment capital are the ingredients of economic progress in the world of today—and tomorrow.

Technology and Economics —the Right Thing at the Right Time

All through this book, the fact is emphasized that land, minerals, energy, and water are available, for the most part, in fixed or decreasing amounts to serve an ever-larger population. Natural resource investments have the basic facts of the situation in their favor. These resources can hardly fail but to go up in value. They are fundamental areas for investment—at the right place and at the right time. But, as most investors of any experience know, you can be right at the wrong time and make no money. The Indians roamed over Texas not knowing that half of the oil reserves of the United States lay beneath their feet. Even if they had known, they couldn't have done anything about it, because the tools and machines with which to drill had not been invented. If they had found oil they would have had little use for it— no cars, no oil burners, no petrochemical plants. These things have to grow up more or less together, by long involved processes.

We have long known there are at least 600 billion barrels of oil in the Athabasca tar sands of Canada. Attempts to develop these reserves in the past failed because technology and economics did not intersect. We had lots of oil, and technology hadn't found a way to get oil out of the tar sands cheaply enough to compete with the oil from wells. Now things are changing, and technology and the demand for oil seem finally to coincide in such a way as to put the Athabasca tar sands in business.

There are believed to be billions of barrels of oil locked in the rocks of the Arctic Islands of Canada (Devon Island and westward). But present drilling costs in such cold and remote areas, plus the problems of getting the oil to market, make the development of this resource unlikely at the moment. Some day the time will be ripe and some companies will make it pay, and this will be a good investment.

There are great quantities of natural gas in the Middle East and North Africa, but without adequate means to get it to market it has limited value. The demand for natural gas in the United States has been rising faster than we have been finding new supplies. But how do you run a pipeline from Arabia to Ohio? Now, as described in the section on NATURAL GAS in this book, ways have been found to transport natural gas by tanker, just like oil, and turn it loose in the pipelines on another continent. Heretofore, when security analysts figured out values of stocks of oil producers with interests in the Middle East and North Africa, gas reserve values have been virtually ignored. But with the advent of gas-carrying tankers, gas reserves in remote areas will have to be considered when the value of a stock is calculated.

The great Mesabi Range of Minnesota had so much ore in it that one of the biggest steel companies in the world ignored iron ore resources potentially in other areas by saying, in effect, "Our supplies of iron ore in Minnesota are virtually inexhaustible." But the demands of two world wars took fantastic quantities of ore, and high grade ore was depleted. Then technology came to the rescue of the Minnesota iron ore industry, and a way was found to economically process low grade taconite. With the price of iron ore higher than previously, and technology finding a way to process taconite, the intersection of these two factors has founded a great new industry.

There are many variations on this theme—that technology and economics intersect sooner or later to create new investment opportunities in our various natural resources. This has happened in the past. Many other such opportunities will be apparent to the informed investor in the future.

Conclusions

Space exploration catches current headlines, but the Earth is going to be home to 99.999999 percent (and more) of us for a long time to come. The population explosion, together with the simple desire of existing populations to raise their standards of living, absolutely guarantees that raw materials and energy sources will be in tremendously increased demand in the immediate future. *We are on the threshold of a demand for natural resources which will be without equal in all history.*

Rising interest in natural resources as investments stems from two things—this tremendous demand for natural resources which is upon us, and the fear of inflation. These two factors are likely to be with us for the indefinite future, and natural resources cannot fail as a group to be prime investments.

The intelligent use of investment capital to develop our natural resources will not only yield a handsome return to the investor. It will also serve the common good in making it possible for our free society to continue to provide for the needs of Man.

Demand for many natural resources will rise almost

geometrically in the foreseeable future. While the general public is looking up at the Moon, wise investors will be looking at the Earth beneath their feet.

Finally, there is for you, only one best investment, an investment which will be with you as long as you live, which is depression-proof, inflation-proof, and cannot be stolen from you. This is the investment you make in yourself. The informed human mind is the greatest resource of all—the key which unlocks all other resource doors. Knowledge is truly power, and today's investor must have a combination of information and imagination—information on the facts of the situation as it now stands, and imagination to see what the possibilities might be in the future. I hope this book will prove a worthy part of this investment in yourself; that it will give you some of the basic facts about our many and varied natural resources, and at the same time stimulate your imagination to visualize the future for these resources and how you might profitably invest in them.

For the alert and informed investor, each day will bring new challenges and new opportunities. Investing in natural resources is both a fundamental and a fascinating activity. And it can be most profitable.

Further Reading

The following list is presented as a sample cross-section of the great variety of literature available on the topic of natural resources. Browsing through these and similar publications may introduce you to new areas to profitably explore. Public and university libraries will have most if not all of these.

Ayres, Eugene, and Scarlott, C. A., 1952, ENERGY SOURCES—THE WEALTH OF THE WORLD. McGraw-Hill Book Co., Inc., New York, 344 p.

Barnett, H. J., 1963, SCARCITY AND GROWTH: THE ECONOMICS OF NATURAL RESOURCE AVAILABILITY. Published for Resources for the Future, Inc., by the Johns Hopkins Press, Baltimore, 298 p.

Bateman, A. M., 1950, ECONOMIC MINERAL DEPOSITS (2nd ed.), John Wiley and Sons, Inc., New York, 916 p.

Brown, Harrison, Bonner, James, and Wier, John, 1957, THE NEXT HUNDRED YEARS. Viking Press, New York, 193 p.

Clawson, Marion (ed.), 1964, NATURAL RESOURCES AND INTERNATIONAL DEVELOPMENT. Published for Resources for the Future, Inc., by the Johns Hopkins Press, Baltimore, 462 p.

Cowan, R. C., 1960, FRONTIERS OF THE SEA. Doubleday and Co., Inc., Garden City, New York, 307 p.

Daniels, Farrington, 1964, DIRECT USE OF THE SUN'S ENERGY. Yale University Press, New Haven, Connecticut, 374 p.

Hatt, Paul (ed.), 1952, WORLD POPULATION AND FUTURE RESOURCES. American Book Co., New York, 262 p.

Hill, R. L. (ed.), 1965, AMERICA 1980. The Graduate School, U. S. Department of Agriculture, Washington, 108 p.

Jarrett, Henry (ed.), 1958, PERSPECTIVES ON CONSERVATION: ESSAYS ON AMERICA'S NATURAL RESOURCES. Published for Resources for the Future, Inc., by the Johns Hopkins Press, Baltimore, 260 p.

Landsberg, H. H., Fischman, L. L., and Fischer, J. L., 1963, RESOURCES IN AMERICA'S FUTURE; PATTERNS OF REQUIREMENTS AND AVAILABILITIES, 1960-2000. Published for Resources for the Future, Inc., by the John Hopkins Press, Baltimore, 1017 p.

Mero, J. L., 1965, THE MINERAL RESOURCES OF THE SEA. Elsevier Publishing Co., New York, 312 p.

Mudd, Stuart (ed.), 1964, THE POPULATION CRISES AND THE USE OF WORLD RESOURCES. Indiana University Press, Bloomington, 562 p.

National Academy of Sciences—National Research Council, 1962, A report to the Committee on Natural Resources of the National Academy of Sciences—National Research Council. RENEWABLE RESOURCES, Publication 1000-A, 127 p; WATER RESOURCES, Publication 1000-B, 35 p.; MINERAL RESOURCES, Publication 1000-C, 32 p.; ENERGY RESOURCES, Publication 1000-D, 141 p.; MARINE RESOURCES, Publication 1000-E, 8 p.; SOCIAL AND ECONOMIC ASPECTS OF NATURAL RESOURCES, Publication 1000-G, 53 p. (Publication 1000-F not published as of this writing.)

Persons, H. H., Jr., 1965, MINING STOCKS OF THE WORLD. Investor's Library Inc., Palisades Park, New Jersey, 95 p.

President's Materials Policy Commission (a report to the President, Wm. S. Paley, Chm.), 1952, RESOURCES FOR FREEDOM: Vol. 1 FOUNDATIONS FOR GROWTH AND SECURITY, 184 p.; Vol. 2 THE OUTLOOK FOR KEY COMMODITIES, 210 p.; Vol. 3 THE OUTLOOK FOR ENERGY SOURCES, 43 p., Vol. 4 THE PROMISE OF TECHNOLOGY, 228 p.; Vol. 5 SELECTED REPORTS TO THE COMMISSION, 154 p. United States Government Printing Office, Washington.

Riley, C. M., 1959, OUR MINERAL RESOURCES. John Wiley and Sons, Inc., New York, 338 p.

Schaefer, M. B., Chm., Committee on Oceanography, National Academy of Sciences—National Research Council, 1964, ECONOMIC BENEFITS FROM OCEANOGRAPHIC RESEARCH. Special Rept. of Comm. on Oceanography, Washington, 50 p.

Smith, F. G. W., and Chapin, Henry, 1954, THE SUN, THE SEA, AND TOMORROW: POTENTIAL SOURCES OF FOOD, ENERGY, AND MINERALS FROM THE SEA. Charles Scribner's Sons, New York, 210 p.

Straus, M. W., 1955, WHY NOT SURVIVE? Simon and Schuster, New York, 272 p.

United States Department of Agriculture, 1949, TREES, 1949 YEARBOOK OF AGRICULTURE. United States Government Printing Office, Washington, 944 p.

——, 1955, WATER, 1955 YEARBOOK OF AGRICULTURE. United States Government Printing Office, Washington, 751 p.

——, 1958, LAND, 1958 YEARBOOK OF AGRICULTURE. United States Government Printing Office, Washington, 605 p.

United States Department of the Interior, 1965, THE RACE FOR INNER SPACE. United States Government Printing Office, Washington, 74 p.

Our several weekly news magazines have timely reports on developments in natural resources, trends in land use, and the impact of population on our resources. (*U. S. News and World Report* is especially good in this regard.) The various financial and business periodicals likewise have such reports, but in greater detail. Quality of the reporting, for the most part, is excellent.

We are also fortunate in having some exceedingly good financial columnists writing for our newspapers. These columnists are becoming more and more widely used by the papers, and this trend is highly desirable. The capital needs for natural resource development in our Nation and around the Free World are, and will continue to be very great. The public must be informed so their money can be invested wisely and effectively. "Investigate, then invest," is a well-known brokerage firm's motto. I could not improve on that recommendation. And remember, "One wise investment is worth years of labor."

Index

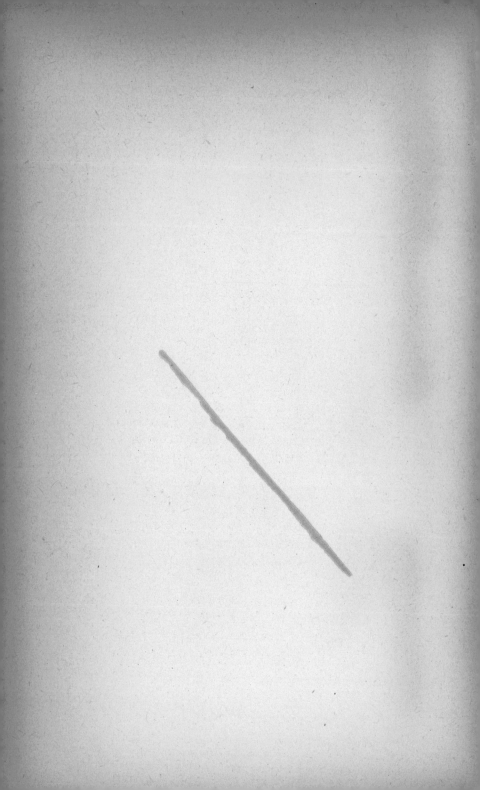